TEST ITEM FILE

JUDI A. LINSLEY
Lourdes College

ESSENTIALS *of*
ANATOMY &
PHYSIOLOGY

SECOND EDITION

MARTINI ◆ BARTHOLOMEW

PRENTICE HALL, Upper Saddle River, NJ 07458

Editor in Chief: Paul F. Corey
Editorial Assistant: Damian Hill
Special Projects Manager: Barbara A. Murray
Production Editor: Shea Oakley
Supplement Cover Manager: Paul Gourhan
Supplement Cover Designer: Liz Nemeth
Manufacturing Manager: Trudy Pisciotti

Printed in the United States of America

10 9 8 7 6 5 4 3 2 1

ISBN 0-13-014666-8

Prentice-Hall International (UK) Limited, London
Prentice-Hall of Australia Pty. Limited, Sydney
Prentice-Hall Canada, Inc., Toronto
Prentice-Hall Hispanoamericana, S.A., Mexico
Prentice-Hall of India Private Limited, New Delhi
Prentice-Hall (Singapore) Pte. Ltd.
Prentice-Hall of Japan, Inc., Tokyo
Editora Prentice-Hall do Brazil, Ltda., Rio de Janeiro

CONTENTS

Prentice Hall: Instructor Support for Test Item Files

This hard copy of the test item file is just one part of Prentice Hall's comprehensive testing support service, which also includes:

1. **Prentice Hall Test Manager:** This powerful computerized testing package is designed for windows 95, Windows 98 and Windows NT. It offers full mouse support, complete question editing capabilities, random test generation, graphics, and printing capabilities.

Prentice Hall Test Manager has removed the guesswork from your next move by incorporating "Screen Wizards" in all five databases. Each one will walk you through the important tasks from start to finish.

In addition to traditional printing capabilities, Prentice Hall Test Manager offers the On-Line Testing System—the most efficient, time-saving examination aid on the market. With just a few keystrokes, the instructor can publish a test to a local area network, correct, record, and return computerized exam results over a variety of LANS.

Prentice Hall Test Manager is designed to assist educators in the recording and processing of results from student exams and assignments. Much more than a computerized gradebook, it combines a powerful database with analytical capabilities so the instructor can generate full sets of various class and individual statistics that allow you to analyze the performance of: test questions, students, an individual class or section, a course with multiple sections, and assessment types such as homework and on-line tests.

Prentice Hall Test Manager is free. To order a specific Prentice Hall Test Manager, you may contact your local sales representative or call our Faculty Support Services Department at 1-800-526-0485. Please identify the main text author and title.

Toll-free **technical support** is offered to all users at 1-800-550-1701.

2.   For those instructors without access to a computer, we offer the **popular Prentice Hall Telephone Testing Service:** It's simple, fast and efficient. Simply pick the questions you'd like on your test from this bank, and call the Testing Service at 1-800-550-1701; outside the US and Canada, call 612-550-1705.

Identify the main text and test questions you'd like, as well as any special instructions. We will create the test (or multiple versions if you wish) and send you a master copy for duplication within 48 hours. Free to adopters for the life of the text.

Chapter 1:   An Introduction to Anatomy and Physiology

Multiple Choice

1. Characteristics of most living organisms include the ability to
   a. grow and reproduce
   b. respond and adapt to their environment
   c. control the external environment
   d. a and b only
   e. all of the above

   Answer: d

2. Multicellular organisms, such as humans, have complex systems to deal with
   a. processing nutrients and eliminating wastes
   b. exchanging gases
   c. transporting materials within the body
   d. a and b only
   e. all of the above

   Answer: e

3. The waste products of metabolism are eliminated through the process of
   a. assimilation
   b. absorption
   c. excretion
   d. digestion
   e. resorption

   Answer: c

4. The study of cells is called
   a. cytology
   b. histology
   c. embryology
   d. physiology
   e. medical anatomy

   Answer: a

5. The study of the general form and superficial markings of an organism is referred to as
   a. gross anatomy
   b. surface anatomy
   c. systemic anatomy
   d. regional anatomy
   e. surgical anatomy

   Answer: b

6. The study of all of the superficial markings of an organism is referred to as
   a. surface anatomy
   b. regional anatomy
   c. surgical anatomy
   d. medical anatomy
   e. radiographic anatomy

   Answer: b

7. An eye, ear, nose, and throat specialist is concerned primarily with the study of
   a. gross anatomy
   b. surface anatomy
   c. microscopic anatomy
   d. systemic anatomy
   e. regional anatomy

   Answer: e

8. The study of the liver is to macroscopic anatomy as the study of the liver cell is to
   a. physiology
   b. regional anatomy
   c. microscopic anatomy
   d. systemic anatomy
   e. radiographic anatomy

   Answer: c

9. The study of life in utero beginning 2 months past fertilization is termed:
   a. histology
   b. embryology
   c. cytology
   d. pathology
   e. organology

   Answer: b

10. The study of tissues is called
    a. gross anatomy
    b. cytology
    c. histology
    d. organology
    e. microbiology

    Answer: c

11. The study of specific organ system function is called
    a. systems physiology
    b. special physiology
    c. cell physiology
    d. histology
    e. physiological chemistry

    Answer: a

12. The branch of physiology that studies functions modified by disease is called
    a. histophysiology
    b. special physiology
    c. system physiology
    d. pathologic physiology
    e. physiological chemistry

    Answer: d

13. The following is a list of several levels of organization that make up the human body:
    1. tissue
    2. cell
    3. organ
    4. molecule
    5. organism
    6. organ system

    The correct order from the smallest to the largest level would be
    a. 2, 4, 1, 3, 6, 5
    b. 4, 2, 1, 3, 6, 5
    c. 4, 2, 1, 6, 3, 5
    d. 4, 2, 3, 1, 6, 5
    e. 2, 1, 4, 3, 5, 6

    Answer: b

14. Support, protection of soft tissue, mineral storage, and blood formation are functions of which system?
    a. integumentary
    b. muscular
    c. skeletal
    d. nervous
    e. none of the above

    Answer: c

15. Locomotion, support of internal organs, and heat production are the functions of which system?
    a. skeletal
    b. muscular
    c. respiratory
    d. lymphatic
    e. cardiovascular

    Answer: b

16. The internal transport of cells and dissolved substances is the function of the
    a. integumentary system
    b. endocrine system
    c. nervous system
    d. cardiovascular system
    e. none of the above

    Answer: d

17. The kidneys and urinary bladder are components of the
    a. endocrine system
    b. digestive system
    c. respiratory system
    d. urinary system
    e. lymphatic system

    Answer: d

18. The pituitary and thyroid glands are components of the
    a. endocrine system
    b. cardiovascular system
    c. respiratory system
    d. lymphatic system
    e. digestive system

    Answer: a

19. Defense against infection and disease is a function of the
    a. cardiovascular system
    b. lymphatic system
    c. respiratory system
    d. urinary system
    e. both a and d

    Answer: b

20. Lungs are to the respiratory system as the spleen is to the
    a. lymphatic system
    b. urinary system
    c. digestive system
    d. cardiovascular system
    e. muscular system

    Answer: a

21. Skin, hair, and nails are associated with the
    a. skeletal system
    b. muscular system
    c. integumentary system
    d. endocrine system
    e. both a and b

    Answer: c

22. The maintenance of a relatively constant internal environment in an organism is termed
    a. positive feedback
    b. homeostasis
    c. negative feedback
    d. effector control
    e. none of the above

    Answer: b

23. When body temperature rises, a center in the brain initiates physiological changes to decrease the body temperature. this regulation mechanism is an example of
    a. negative feedback
    b. positive feedback
    c. non-homeostatic regulation
    d. diagnostic regulation
    e. disease

    Answer: a

24. The increasingly forceful labor contractions that lead to childbirth are an example of this type of mechanism
    a. receptor activation
    b. effector shutdown
    c. negative feedback
    d. positive feedback
    e. none of the above

    Answer: d

25. In general, the nervous system
    a. helps to maintain homeostasis
    b. responds rapidly
    c. directs very specific responses
    d. has short-term effects
    e. all of the above

    Answer: e

26. Which of the following is not characteristic of the endocrine system?
    a. releases chemical messengers called hormones
    b. produces a more rapid response to body changes than the nervous system
    c. can produce effects that last for days or longer
    d. can produce an effect that involves several organs or tissues at the same time
    e. is an important homeostatic system

    Answer: b

27. A person who is facing forward with arms at the sides and palms facing forward is said to be in the
    a. supine position
    b. prone position
    c. anatomical position
    d. frontal position
    e. sagittal position

    Answer: c

28. Which indicates the front of the body?
    a. anterior
    b. posterior
    c. dorsal
    d. ventral
    e. both a and d

    Answer: e

29. Which of the following is lateral to the nose?
    a. eyes
    b. forehead
    c. scalp
    d. chin
    e. chest

    Answer: a

30. The wrist is considered _____ to the elbow.
    a. proximal
    b. distal
    c. lateral
    d. medial
    e. none of the above

    Answer: b

31. The chest is _____ to the umbilicus.
    a. anterior
    b. superior
    c. posterior
    d. inferior
    e. medial

    Answer: b

32. Which of the following regions corresponds to the lower back?
    a. pelvic
    b. cephalic
    c. gluteal
    d. lumbar
    e. thoracic

    Answer: d

33. Which of the following regions corresponds to the upper arm?
    a. cervical
    b. brachial
    c. antebrachial
    d. femoral
    e. pedal

    Answer: b

34. A cut passing through the midline of the body that divides it into equal left and right halves is known as this type of plane:
    a. frontal
    b. coronal
    c. transverse
    d. midsagittal
    e. parasagittal

    Answer: d

35. The cranial cavity and spinal cavity would be found in the
    a. dorsal body cavity
    b. peritoneal cavity
    c. pleural cavity
    d. ventral body cavity
    e. abdominopelvic cavity

    Answer: a

36. The diaphragm separates the _____ cavity from the _____
    cavity.
    a. pleura; mediastinum
    b. thoracic; abdominopelvic
    c. pericardial; pleural
    d. abdominal; pelvic
    e. pericardial sac; pericardial

    Answer: b

37. The thoracic cavity contains the
    a. abdominal cavity
    b. pericardial cavity
    c. pelvic cavity
    d. cranium
    e. all of the above

    Answer: b

38. The mediastinum separates _____ from the _____.
    a. the pleural cavity; coelom
    b. the thoracic cavity; peritoneal cavity
    c. one pleural cavity; other pleural cavity
    d. the abdominal cavity; pelvic cavity
    e. the pericardial sac; pericardial cavity

    Answer: c

39. The peritoneal cavity contains the
    a. pelvic cavity
    b. pleural cavity
    c. cranial cavity
    d. ventral body cavity
    e. spinal cavity

    Answer: a

40. Mary, who is 6 months pregnant, goes to her physician for a test to check the development of her fetus. The physician uses a device that employs sound waves to produce an image of the fetus. this technique is known as a/an
    a. x-ray
    b. CT scan
    c. MRI
    d. ultrasound
    e. radiography

    Answer: d

41. A diagnostic technique that employs a computer to produce sectional views of the body from x-rays is the
    a. angiogram
    b. radiograph
    c. CT scan
    d. MRI
    e. ultrasound

    Answer: c

42. Which sectional plane could divide the body so that the face remains intact?
    a. sagittal plane
    b. coronal plane
    c. equatorial plane
    d. midsagittal plane
    e. none of the above

    Answer: b

43. Which of the following tissues would be the most radio-dense?
    a. muscle
    b. blood
    c. fat
    d. bone
    e. nervous

    Answer: d

44. Organs in which of the following cavities would show the effects or symptoms first of an enlarging benign tumor?
    a. dorsal cavity
    b. ventral cavity
    c. abdominal cavity
    d. pelvic cavity
    e. pleural cavity

    Answer: a

45. Cells are considered the smallest units of life because
    a. cells are composed of organelles, each of which is responsible for a particular "life-giving" function.
    b. cells are composed of atoms which, chemically, are the smallest units of structure.
    c. cells are composed of molecules which, chemically, are the smallest units of structure.
    d. the cell is not considered the smallest unit of life.
    e. a and c are correct

    Answer: a

46. A chemical imbalance in a heart muscle cell can cause the heart to cease pumping blood, which in turn will cause other tissues and organs to cease functioning. This observation supports the view that
    a. all organisms are composed of cells
    b. all levels of organization within an organism are interdependent
    c. chemical molecules make up cells
    d. all cells are independent of each other
    e. congenital defects can be life threatening

    Answer: b

47. Each of the following is an example of negative feedback **except** one. Identify the exception.
    a. Increased pressure in the aorta triggers mechanisms to lower blood pressure.
    b. A rise in blood calcium levels triggers the release of a hormone that lowers blood calcium levels.
    c. A rise in estrogen during the menstrual cycle increases the number of progesterone receptors in the uterus.
    d. Increased blood sugar stimulates the release of a hormone from the pancreas that stimulates the liver to store blood sugar.
    e. A decrease in body temperature triggers a neural response that initiates physiological changes to increase body temperature.

    Answer: c

48. The human body is, in essence, an interplay of eleven <u>systems</u> which includes the following:
    a. the integumentary, skeletal, muscular, and nervous
    b. the nervous, lymphatic, respiratory, and lungs
    c. the cardiovascular, reproductive, and ovaries
    d. the endocrine, urinary, and pituitary
    e. none of the above

    Answer: a

49. In dealing with physiology, <u>function</u> is related to its
    a. form
    b. location
    c. size
    d. cavity
    e. system

Answer: a

50. The chemical, or molecular, level of organization begins with
    _____, which then form _____.
    a. molecules; atoms
    b. cells; tissues
    c. atoms; molecules
    d. organs; systems
    e. macromolecules; molecules

Answer: c

51. This portion of the body contains the head, neck, and trunk.
    a. appendicular
    b. thoracic
    c. axial
    d. dorsal
    e. ventral

Answer: c

52. This portion of the body contains the arms and legs.
    a. axial
    b. appendicular
    c. ventral
    d. dorsal
    e. thoracic

Answer: b

53. The two primary cavitis of the body include the _____ and the
    _____.
    a. axial cavity; appendicular cavity
    b. posterior cavity; dorsal cavity
    c. anterior cavity; ventral cavity
    d. organ cavity; thoracic cavity
    e. anterior cavity; posterior cavity

Answer: e

54. Organs situated within the mediastinum include:
    a. heart, lungs, and esophagus
    b. thymus, esophagus, and trachea
    c. thyroid, lungs, and liver
    d. pancreas, liver, and spleen
    e. stomach, pancreas, and heart

    Answer: b

55. The heart is surrounded by the _____ membrane.
    a. pericardial
    b. peritoneal
    c. visceral
    d. serous
    e. pleural

    Answer: a

56. The membrane covering the surface of the lung is named the
    a. parietal pleura
    b. visceral pleura
    c. pericardial sac
    d. visceral peritoneum
    e. serous membrane

    Answer: b

57. The membrane covering the surface of the heart is referred to as the
    a. visceral pleura
    b. parietal peritoneum
    c. visceral pericardium
    d. serous membrane
    e. mediastinum

    Answer: c

58. Magnetic resonance imaging (MRI) makes use of
    a. radio waves
    b. sound waves
    c. x-rays
    d. microwaves
    e. echo waves

    Answer: a

Fill-In-The-Blank

59. The appearance of characteristic cellular specializations during development is termed _____.

    Answer: differentiation

60. The study of body structure is called _____.

    Answer: anatomy

61. The branch of biological science that deals with how body parts function is called _____.

    Answer: physiology

62. The tendency for physiological systems to stabilize internal conditions with respect to the external environment is called _____.

    Answer: homeostasis

63. Homeostatic regulation usually involves a(n) _____ that is sensitive to a particular stimulus and a(n) _____ whose activity has an effect on the same stimulus.

    Answer: receptor; effector

64. In _____ feedback, the initial stimulus produces a response that escalates the stimulus.

    Answer: positive

65. When homeostatic mechanisms fail, an individual will experience with symptoms of _____, or illness.

    Answer: disease

66. A person lying face down in the anatomical position is said to be in the _____ position.

    Answer: prone

67. A person lying face up in the anatomical position is said to be in the _____ position.

    Answer: supine

68. A cut parallel to the midsagittal line would produce a _____ section.

    Answer: parasagittal

69. The term _____ refers to the combination of anabolic and catabolic activities that occur within a living organism.

    Answer: metabolism

70. Using anatomical terms of direction, supply the word that would make the sentence correct.
The stomach is _____ to the lungs.

    Answer: inferior

71. Using anatomical terms of direction, supply the word that would make the sentence correct.
The hand is _____ to the elbow.

    Answer: distal

72. Using anatomical terms of direction, supply the word that would make the sentence correct.
The knee is _____ to the foot.

    Answer: proximal

Essay

73. It is a warm day and you feel a little chilled. On checking your temperature, you find that your body temperature is 1.5 degrees below normal. Suggest some possible reasons for this situation.

    Answer:
    There are several reasons why your body temperature may have dropped. Your body may be losing heat faster than it is being produced. This, however, is more likely to occur on a cool day. Various chemical factors, such as hormones, may have caused a decrease in your metabolic rate and thus your body is not producing as much heat as it normally would. Alternatively, you may be suffering from an infection that has temporarily changed the setpoint of the body's "thermostat." This would seem to be the most likely explanation considering the circumstances given in the question.

Matching

74. Match the organ system in the first column with its primary function in the second column.

    _____1. integumentary system   A. defense against infection
    _____2. muscular system   B. protection from environment
    _____3. endocrine system   C. processing of food
    _____4. cardiovascular system   D. internal transport of materials
    _____5. respiratory system   E. elimination of excess water
    _____6. urinary system   F. production of sex cells
    _____7. reproductive system   G. support and protection
    _____8. skeletal system   H. delivery of air for gas exchange
    _____9. nervous system   I. locomotion and heat production
    _____10. lymphatic system   J. directing responses to stimuli
    _____11. digestive system   K. directing long-term changes

Answer: 1-B, 2-I, 3-K, 4-D, 5-H, 6-E, 7-F, 8-G, 9-J, 10-A, 11-C

75. Match the item in the first column with its primary function in the second column.

    _____1. epidermis   A. propels blood
    _____2. bone marrow   B. covers surface
    _____3. skeletal muscles   C. controls nervous activities
    _____4. brain   D. provides skeletal movement
    _____5. heart   E. site of blood cell production

Answer: 1-B, 2-E, 3-D, 4-C, 5-A

76. Match the body cavity in the first column with the organ it contains in the second column.

    _____1. cranial cavity   A. liver
    _____2. spinal cavity   B. brain
    _____3. thoracic cavity   C. urinary bladder
    _____4. abdominal cavity   D. lungs
    _____5. pelvic cavity   E. spinal cord

Answer: 1-B, 2-E, 3-D, 4-A, 5-C

77. Match the organ system in the first column with the organ found within that system in the second column.

    _____1. endocrine system   A. arteries
    _____2. urinary system   B. liver
    _____3. digestive system   C. pituitary gland
    _____4. skeletal system   D. ligaments
    _____5. circulatory system   E. urethra

Answer: 1-C, 2-E, 3-B, 4-D, 5-A

78. Match the body regions in the first column with the locations in the second column.

     ____1. axillary   A. navel
     ____2. cervical   B. ear
     ____3. gluteal   C. arm pit
     ____4. umbilical   D. neck
     ____5. otic   E. buttocks

Answer: 1-C, 2-D, 3-E, 4-A, 5-B

Chapter 2:   The Chemical Level of Organization

Multiple Choice

1. The smallest units of matter are
   a. atoms
   b. molecules
   c. protons
   d. neutrons
   e. electrons

   Answer: a

2. Which of the following would have the largest size?
   a. an atom
   b. a molecule
   c. a proton
   d. a neutron
   e. an electron

   Answer: b

3. Isotopes of an element differ in the number of
   a. protons in the nucleus
   b. electrons in the nucleus
   c. neutrons in the nucleus
   d. electron clouds
   e. energy levels they contain

   Answer: c

4. The atomic number represents the number of
   a. protons in an atom
   b. electrons in an ion
   c. neutrons in an atom
   d. protons and neutrons
   e. neutrons and electrons

   Answer: a

5. All atoms with the same atomic number are grouped into
   a. molecules
   b. cells
   c. compounds
   d. elements
   e. none of the above

   Answer: d

6. The atomic weight of an element indicates the number of
   a. protons in the nucleus
   b. neutrons in the nucleus
   c. electrons in the outer shells
   d. protons and neutrons in the nucleus
   e. protons and electrons in an atom

   Answer: d

7. The chemical behavior of an atom is determined by
   a. the number of protons
   b. the number of neutrons
   c. the number and arrangement of electrons
   d. the size of the atom
   e. the mass of the atom

   Answer: c

8. A substance containing atoms of different elements that are bonded together is called a(n)
   a. molecule
   b. compound
   c. mixture
   d. isotope
   e. none of the above

   Answer: b

9. Ions with a positive charge are called
   a. cations
   b. anions
   c. radicals
   d. polyatomic ions
   e. none of the above

   Answer: a

10. In living cells, the weakest bond between two or more atoms is the
    a. ionic bond
    b. covalent bond
    c. polar bond
    d. metallic bond
    e. hydrogen bond

    Answer: e

11. Ionic bonds are formed when
    a. atoms share electrons
    b. cations and anions are held together by their opposite charges
    c. a pair of electrons is shared unequally by two atoms
    d. hydrogen forms bonds with negatively charged atoms in the same or different molecules
    e. two or more atoms lose electrons at the same time

    Answer: b

12. In a molecule of nitrogen, three pairs of electrons are shared by two nitrogen atoms. The type of bond that is formed would be an example of a
    a. single covalent bond
    b. double covalent bond
    c. triple covalent bond
    d. polar covalent bond
    e. hydrogen bond

    Answer: c

13. If a pair of electrons is unequally shared between two atoms, this type of bond occurs:
    a. single covalent bond
    b. double covalent bond
    c. triple covalent bond
    d. polar covalent bond
    e. hydrogen bond

    Answer: d

14. Elements that have full outer shells of electrons
    a. will form many compounds
    b. will normally form anions
    c. will normally form cations
    d. frequently form hydrogen bonds
    e. are inert

    Answer: e

15. Which of the following statements about the reaction $H_2 + Cl_2 \rightarrow 2HCl$ is not correct?
    a. H_2 and Cl_2 are the reactants
    b. HCl is the product
    c. one molecule of hydrogen contains 2 atoms
    d. one molecule of chlorine contains 2 atoms
    e. all of the above are correct

    Answer: e

16. AB $\rightarrow$ A + B is to decomposition as A + B $\rightarrow$ AB is to
    a. exchange
    b. synthesis
    c. combustion
    d. replacement
    e. metabolism

Answer: b

17. The reaction N_2 + $3H_2$ $\rightarrow$ $2NH_3$ would be an example of a(n)
    a. exchange reaction
    b. decomposition reaction
    c. synthesis reaction
    d. enzyme reaction
    e. metabolic reaction

Answer: c

18. Chemical reactions that require an input of energy exceeding that released, such as the addition of heat, are said to be
    a. endergonic
    b. activated
    c. exergonic
    d. neutral
    e. none of the above

Answer: a

19. A solution containing equal numbers of hydrogen ions and hydroxide ions is
    a. acidic
    b. basic
    c. neutral
    d. alkaline
    e. none of the above

Answer: c

20. Which of the following substances would be least acidic?
    a. lemon juice, pH = 5.5
    b. urine, pH = 6
    c. tomato juice, pH = 4
    d. white wine, pH = 3
    e. stomach secretions, pH = 2

Answer: b

21. If a substance has a pH that is greater than 7, it is
    a. neutral
    b. acidic
    c. alkaline
    d. a buffer
    e. a salt

Answer: c

22. An important buffer in body fluids is
    a. NaCl
    b. NaOH
    c. HCl
    d. $NaHCO_3$ (sodium bicarbonate)
    e. H_2O

Answer: d

23. All of the compounds that can be synthesized or broken down by chemical reactions inside the body are called
    a. inorganic compounds
    b. organic compounds
    c. nutrients
    d. metabolites
    e. enzymes

Answer: d

24. Each of the following is an example of an inorganic compound **except** one. Identify the exception.
    a. water
    b. acids
    c. bases
    d. salts
    e. enzymes

Answer: e

25. Organic compounds in the human body contain all of the following **except**
    a. hydrogen
    b. oxygen
    c. carbon
    d. calcium
    e. none of these

Answer: d

26. Which of the following statements about water is not correct?
    a. It is composed of polar molecules.
    b. It is responsible for about 2/3 of the mass of the human body.
    c. It has a relatively low heat capacity.
    d. It dissolves many compounds.
    e. It contains hydrogen bonds.

    Answer: c

27. During ionization, water molecules disrupt the ionic bonds of a solute resulting in a mixture of ions. These ions are called
    a. cations
    b. anions
    c. dissociates
    d. electrolytes
    e. anti-ions

    Answer: d

28. In the body, inorganic compounds
    a. serve as buffers
    b. make up proteins
    c. are important nutrients
    d. are structural components of cells
    e. all of the above

    Answer: a

29. Inorganic acids in the body include:
    a. hydrochloric
    b. carbonic
    c. sulfuric
    d. phosphoric
    e. all of the above

    Answer: e

30. Carbohydrate molecules
    a. serve as structural components of human cells
    b. form the regulatory molecules known as enzymes
    c. are the body's most important source of energy
    d. help to protect vital organs from damage
    e. contain the genetic information found in cells

    Answer: c

31. The most important metabolic fuel molecule in the body is
    a. sucrose
    b. starch
    c. protein
    d. vitamin B12
    e. glucose

    Answer: e

32. A polysaccharide that is formed in the liver and muscle to store glucose
    is
    a. starch
    b. glycogen
    c. fructose
    d. cellulose
    e. sucrose

    Answer: b

33. The group of organic compounds containing carbon, hydrogen, and oxygen
    in a near 1:2:1 ratio is defined as a
    a. carbohydrate
    b. lipid
    c. protein
    d. nucleic acid
    e. none of the above

    Answer: a

34. Lipids
    a. form essential structural components of cells
    b. provide roughly twice the energy as carbohydrates
    c. help to maintain body temperature
    d. help to cushion delicate organs from damage
    e. all of the above

    Answer: e

35. A fatty acid that contains three double covalent bonds in its carbon
    chain is said to be
    a. saturated
    b. polyunsaturated
    c. monounsaturated
    d. hydrogenated
    e. carboxylated

    Answer: b

36. The most common fat found in the human body is in the form of
    a. steroids
    b. phospholipids
    c. triglycerides
    d. hormones
    e. monoglycerides

    Answer: c

37. Each of the following is a function of proteins **except** one. Identify the exception.
    a. support
    b. transport
    c. metabolic regulation
    d. movement
    e. absorption

    Answer: e

38. You would expect to find a peptide bond linking
    a. two simple sugars
    b. one amino acid to an amino group of another
    c. two nucleotides
    d. a fatty acid and a glycerol molecule
    e. a cholesterol molecule and a fatty acid molecule

    Answer: b

39. Each amino acid differs from others in the
    a. number of central carbon atoms
    b. size of the amino group
    c. number of carboxyl groups
    d. nature of the R group
    e. number of peptide bonds in the molecule

    Answer: d

40. The molecules that store and process information at the molecular level are the
    a. proteins
    b. nucleic acids
    c. carbohydrates
    d. steroids
    e. lipids

    Answer: b

41. Nucleic acids are composed of units called
    a. amino acids
    b. simple sugars
    c. fatty acids
    d. adenosines
    e. nucleotides

Answer: e

42. A nucleotide consists of
    a. a five-carbon sugar and a phosphate group
    b. a five-carbon sugar and a nitrogen base
    c. a phosphate group and a nitrogenous base
    d. a five-carbon sugar, a nitrogenous base, and a phosphate group
    e. a five-carbon sugar and an amino acid

Answer: d

43. According to the rules of complementary base pairing, a nucleotide containing the base, cytosine, would only pair with a nucleotide containing the base
    a. thymine
    b. adenine
    c. uracil
    d. cytosine
    e. guanine

Answer: e

44. The most important high energy compound in cells is
    a. glucose
    b. fructose
    c. protein
    d. adenosine triphosphate
    e. deoxyribose

Answer: d

45. Chemical reactions that occur in the human body are controlled by special catalytic molecules called
    a. enzymes
    b. cytozymes
    c. cofactors
    d. activators
    e. none of the above

Answer: a

46. Enzymes
    a. are proteins
    b. function as biological catalysts
    c. lower the activation energy for a reaction
    d. affect the rate of a chemical reaction
    e. all of the above

    Answer: e

47. Substrate molecules bind to enzymes at the
    a. amino group sites
    b. active sites
    c. carboxyl group sites
    d. reactant sites
    e. none of the above

    Answer: b

48. An excess of hydrogen ions in the body fluids can have disastrous
    results because
    a. excess hydrogen ions can break chemical bonds
    b. excess hydrogen ions can change the shape of large complex molecules,
       rendering them non-functional
    c. excess hydrogen ions can disrupt tissue functions
    d. excess hydrogen ions can kill living cells
    e. all of the above

    Answer: e

49. A dehydration synthesis reaction between glycerol and a single fatty
    acid would yield a
    a. steroid
    b. hormone
    c. monoglyceride
    d. diglyceride
    e. triglyceride

    Answer: c

50. If an element is composed of atoms with an atomic number of 6 and a mass
    number of 14, then a neutral atom of this element contains
    a. 6 protons
    b. 6 neutrons
    c. 8 electrons
    d. 14 protons
    e. 14 electrons

    Answer: a

51. When electrons are transferred from one atom to another, and the two atoms unite as a result of the electrostatic attraction,
    a. an ion is formed
    b. a molecule is formed
    c. a hydrogen bond is formed
    d. an ionic bond is formed
    e. a covalent bond is formed

    Answer: d

52. Calcium atoms have two electrons in the outermost shell. As a result, one would expect calcium to form ions with a charge of
    a. +1
    b. +2
    c. -1
    d. -2
    e. none of the above

    Answer: b

53. Each of the following statements concerning hydrogen bonds is true **except** one. Identify the exception.
    a. Hydrogen bonds are strong attractive forces between hydrogen atoms and negatively charged atoms.
    b. Hydrogen bonds can occur within a single molecule.
    c. Hydrogen bonds can form between neighboring molecules.
    d. Hydrogen bonds are important forces for holding large molecules together.
    e. Hydrogen bonds are responsible for many of the unique properties of water.

    Answer: a

54. In an exergonic reaction
    a. large molecules are broken down into smaller ones.
    b. small molecules are assembled into larger ones.
    c. molecules are rearranged to form new molecules.
    d. molecules move from reactants to products and back.
    e. energy is released during the reaction.

    Answer: e

55. An inorganic compound, when place in water, dissociates 99% forming hydrogen ions and anions. This substance would be a
    a. strong base
    b. weak base
    c. strong acid
    d. weak acid
    e. salt

    Answer: c

56. When two monosaccharides undergo a dehydration synthesis
    a. a new monosaccharide is formed.
    b. a disaccharide is formed.
    c. a polysaccharide is formed.
    d. a starch is formed.
    e. hydrolysis occurs.

    Answer: b

57. The nucleic acid RNA
    a. is double stranded.
    b. contains uracil in place of thymine.
    c. contains the pentose deoxyribose.
    d. contains protein bases.
    e. synthesizes lipids.

    Answer: b

58. If a polypeptide contains 10 peptide bonds, how many amino acids does it contain?
    a. 0
    b. 5
    c. 10
    d. 11
    e. 12

    Answer: d

59. The branch of science that deals with the interaction of living and non-living materials is
    a. biology
    b. pathology
    c. botany
    d. geology
    e. chemistry

    Answer: e

60. The best definition of <u>matter</u> is anything that
    a. has weight and takes up space
    b. takes up time and has mass
    c. has mass and is solid
    d. has weight and is liquid
    e. is comprised of organic materials

    Answer: a

61. Which of the following is not a principal element in the human body?
    a. hydrogen
    b. sulfur
    c. iron
    d. iodine
    e. copper

    Answer: e

62. An unstable isotope that emits subatomic particles spontaneously is called
    a. a radioisotope
    b. a proton
    c. an ion
    d. an atom
    e. a gamma ray

    Answer: a

Fill-In-The-Blank

63. A(n) _____ contains atoms with the same atomic number.

    Answer: element

64. The atomic center is called the _____.

    Answer: nucleus

65. Electrons in an atom occupy an orderly series of electron shells or _____ _____.

    Answer: energy levels

66. A molecule containing two or more elements in combination is called a(n) _____.

    Answer: compound

67. Ions with a positive charge are called _____.

    Answer: cations

68. ions with a negative charge are called _____.

    Answer: anions

69. In a _____ reaction, bonds between atoms are broken and atoms are rearranged into new combinations.

    Answer: chemical

70. Chemical reactions that release energy are said to be _____.

    Answer: exergonic

71. Chemical reactions that require an input of energy are said to be _____.

    Answer: endergonic

72. The _____ of a solution is the concentration of hydrogen ions.

    Answer: pH

73. _____ are compounds that maintain pH of solutions within given limits.

    Answer: Buffers

74. _____ compounds contain carbon, hydrogen, and usually oxygen.

    Answer: Organic

75. _____ compounds do not contain carbon as the primary structural atom.

    Answer: Inorganic

76. A(n) _____ is a homogenous mixture containing a solvent and a solute.

    Answer: solution

77. _____ are soluble inorganic compounds whose ions will conduct an electric current in solutions.

    Answer: Electrolytes

78. Amino acids contain a central carbon atom adjacent to a(n) _____ group and a(n) _____ _____ group.

    Answer: amine; carboxylic acid

79. The molecule DNA contains the five-carbon sugar _____.

    Answer: deoxyribose

80. The molecule RNA contains the five-carbon sugar _____.

    Answer: ribose

81. A _____ bond is a covalent bond that stores an unusually large amount of energy.

    Answer: high-energy

82. The hydrolysis of ATP yields the molecule _____.

    Answer: ADP

83. Chemical reactions that occur in the human body are controlled by special protein molecules called _____.

    Answer: enzymes

84. In living cells, complex reactions proceed in a sequence of interlocking steps called a metabolic _____.

    Answer: pathway

85. The branch of science that concerns itself with the chemistry of living things is referred to as _____.

    Answer: biochemistry

86. Atoms of the same element have the same number of _____, but may have a different number of _____.

    Answer: protons; neutrons

Essay

87. Why is it life-threatening to have a high fever?

    Answer:
    A high body temperature can be life-threatening because the heat can cause certain proteins, such as vital enzymes, to become denatured. When this occurs, the proteins become non-functional and if they catalyze reactions that are necessary for life, life will cease.

88. A certain reaction pathway consists of four steps. How would decreasing the amount of enzyme that catalyzes the second step affect the amount of product produced at the end of the pathway?

    Answer:
    Decreasing the amount of enzyme at the second step would slow down the whole series of reactions because less substrate would be available for the next two steps. The net result would be a decrease in the amount of product.

89. How does the DNA molecule control the appearance and function of a cell?

    Answer:
    The DNA molecule controls the manufacture of enzymes and structural proteins. By controlling the manufacture of structural proteins, the DNA is able to influence the physical appearance of a cell. By controlling the production of enzymes, the DNA is able to control all aspects of cellular metabolism and thus control the activity and biological functions of the cell.

Matching

90. Match the terms in the first column with the definitions in the second.

    _____1. acid   A. solute that removes hydrogen ions
    _____2. base   B. solute that dissociates to release hydrogen ions
    _____3. buffer   C. consists of a fluid solvent and dissolved solutes
    _____4. solution   D. compounds that stabilize pH
    _____5. water   E. the most important body constituent

    Answer:
    1 - B
    2 - A
    3 - D
    4 - C
    5 - E

Free Response

91. Identify the following compounds as organic (O) or inorganic (I):

    1._____ glucose
    2._____ sucrose
    3._____ water
    4._____ starch
    5._____ carbon dioxide

    Answer:
    1 - O
    2 - O
    3 - I
    4 - O
    5 - I

92. Identify the following carbohydrates as monosaccharides (M), disaccharides (D), or polysaccharides (P)

    1._____ glucose
    2._____ sucrose
    3._____ fructose
    4._____ lactose
    5._____ glycogen

    Answer:
    1 - M
    2 - D
    3 - M
    4 - D
    5 - P

93. Identify the lipid type for the following representative lipids. Use FA for fatty acids, G for glycerides, S for steroids, and P for phospholipids.

    1._____ lauric acid
    2._____ cholesterol
    3._____ diglycerides
    4._____ triglycerides
    5._____ monoglycerides

    Answer:
    1 - FA
    2 - S
    3 - G
    4 - G
    5 - G

Chapter 3:   Cell Structure and Function

Multiple Choice

1. Which of the following is **not** a concept of the cell theory?
   a. Cells are the basic structural unit of life.
   b. Cells are the site of homeostatic control.
   c. Organelles are the basic function unit of life.
   d. Cells are produced by mitosi.
   e. all the above are correct

   Answer: c

2. The basic structural and functional unit of the human body is
   a. protein
   b. the cell
   c. tissue
   d. the organ
   e. the organ system

   Answer: b

3. The watery medium that surrounds a cell is known as
   a. cytosol
   b. protoplasm
   c. extracellular fluid
   d. cytoplasm
   e. a colloidal gel

   Answer: c

4. Which of the following terms is **not** used to define the structure that separates the contents of a human cell from its surrounding medium?
   a. a cell wall
   b. a cell membrane
   c. plasma membrane
   d. a cell boundary
   e. all of the above are used

   Answer: a

5. Which of the following is **not** a function of the cell membrane?
   a. separation of the cytoplasm from the extracellular fluid
   b. regulation of exchange of materials with the environment
   c. sensitivity to changes in the extracellular fluid
   d. structural support
   e. controling movement into the nucleus

   Answer: e

6. Structurally, the plasma membrane
   a. is composed of a bilayer of proteins
   b. is composed of a bilayer of lipids
   c. is composed of only carbohydrate molecules
   d. is a complex combination of carbohydrates and proteins
   e. is a complex combination of carbohydrates and lipids

Answer: b

7. Which of the following is **not** a function of membrane proteins?
   a. They bind to specific extracellular molecules to trigger a cellular change.
   b. They regulate the passage of ions.
   c. They are carrier molecules for various solutes.
   d. They serve as anchors or stabilizers for the cell membrane.
   e. They produce energy.

Answer: e

8. Cell membranes are said to be
   a. impermeable
   b. freely permeable
   c. selectively permeable
   d. actively permeable
   e. none of the above

Answer: c

9. The movement of oxygen from an area of high concentration to an area of low concentration is an example of
   a. osmosis
   b. active transport
   c. diffusion
   d. facilitated diffusion
   e. filtration

Answer: c

10. The movement of water across a membrane from an area of low solute concentration to an area of higher solute concentration is known as
    a. osmosis
    b. active transport
    c. diffusion
    d. facilitated diffusion
    e. filtration

Answer: a

11. Water molecules and small ions enter a cell through
    a. channels in some cell membrane proteins
    b. receptor proteins
    c. lipid channels
    d. anchor proteins
    e. all of the above

Answer: a

12. A solution that contains a lower solute concentration than the cytoplasm of a cell is called
    a. holotonic
    b. hypertonic
    c. isotonic
    d. hypotonic
    e. semitonic

Answer: d

13. Crenation occurs when a blood cell is placed in a
    a. isotonic solution
    b. hypertonic solution
    c. hypotonic solution
    d. holotonic solution
    e. none of the above

Answer: b

14. The process by which molecules such as glucose are moved into cells along their concentration gradient with the help of membrane-bound carrier proteins is called
    a. osmosis
    b. passive transport
    c. active transport
    d. osmosis
    e. exocytosis

Answer: b

15. Facilitated diffusion differs from ordinary diffusion in that facilitated diffusion
    a. expends no ATP
    b. moves molecules from an area of higher concentration to lower concentration
    c. limits the rate of molecular movement by limiting the number of available carrier molecules
    d. never eliminates the concentration gradient
    e. does not limit the rate of molecular movement by the number of available carrier molecules

Answer: c

16. A process that requires cellular energy to move a substance against its concentration gradient is called
    a. active transport
    b. passive transport
    c. facilitated transport
    d. osmosis
    e. diffusion

    Answer: a

17. The packaging of extracellular materials in a vesicle at the cell surface for importation into the cell is called
    a. osmosis
    b. active transport
    c. facilitated transport
    d. endocytosis
    e. an ion exchange pump

    Answer: d

18. The process by which vesicles containing solid objects such as bacteria are formed on the surface of a cell for transport into the cell is called
    a. pinocytosis
    b. phagocytosis
    c. exocytosis
    d. receptor-mediated endocytosis
    e. none of the above

    Answer: b

19. Each of the following is an example of a non-membranous organelle **except** one. Identify the exception.
    a. lysosomes
    b. cilia
    c. centrioles
    d. ribosomes
    e. cytoskeleton

    Answer: a

20. Components of the cytoskeleton may include
    a. microfilaments
    b. thick filaments
    c. actin
    d. myosin
    e. all of the above

    Answer: e

21. Tubulin is to microtubules as actin is to
    a. ribosomes
    b. microfilaments
    c. mysoin
    d. flagella
    e. microvilli

    Answer: b

22. Which of the following cytoskeleton components are responsible for the movement of chromosomes during cell division?
    a. microfilaments
    b. cilia
    c. thick filaments
    d. microtubules
    e. all of the above

    Answer: d

23. Flagella move a cell through a fluid medium. What moves the fluid medium across the surface of cells?
    a. centrioles
    b. thick filaments
    c. cilia
    d. ribosomes
    e. endoplasmic reticula

    Answer: c

24. Most of the ATP required to power cellular operations is produced in the
    a. ribosomes
    b. endoplasmic reticulum
    c. nucleus
    d. mitochondria
    e. Golgi apparatus

    Answer: d

25. The fluid within mitochondria is called
    a. cristae
    b. cytosol
    c. cytoplasm
    d. matrix
    e. none of the above

    Answer: d

26. The components of ribosomes are formed by
    a. endoplasmic reticulum
    b. Golgi complex
    c. lysosomes
    d. mitochondria
    e. nucleoli

    Answer: e

27. Synthesis of lipids takes place in the
    a. ribosomes
    b. rough ER
    c. smooth ER
    d. Golgi apparatus
    e. mitochondria

    Answer: c

28. Renewal or modification of the cell membrane is a function of the
    a. microtubules
    b. mitochondria
    c. rough ER
    d. ribosomes
    e. Golgi apparatus

    Answer: e

29. When activated, lysosomes function in
    a. the formation of new cell membranes
    b. the synthesis of proteins
    c. digestion of foreign material
    d. the synthesis of lipids
    e. cell division

    Answer: c

30. The cell's DNA is located in the
    a. ribosomes
    b. nucleolus
    c. lysosomes
    d. nucleus
    e. Golgi complex

    Answer: d

31. The control center for cellular operations is the
    a. nucleus
    b. nucleolus
    c. cell membrane
    d. Golgi apparatus
    e. none of the above

    Answer: a

32. The complex structures of DNA and protein found in the cell nucleus are called
    a. nucleoplasms
    b. chromosomes
    c. mitochondria
    d. nucleolemmas
    e. nucleoli

    Answer: b

33. The nucleus stores all the information needed to synthesize which of the following molecules?
    a. carbohydrates
    b. lipids
    c. proteins
    d. phospholipids
    e. none of the above

    Answer: c

34. All of the triplet codes needed to produce a specific polypeptide chain are found in a(n)
    a. chromosome
    b. gene
    c. codon
    d. anticodon
    e. none of the above

    Answer: b

35. As each codon binds at the active site of a ribosome, it interacts with another molecule. This molecule is called
    a. DNA
    b. mRNA
    c. ribosomal RNA
    d. tRNA
    e. rough ER

    Answer: d

36. Which of the following sequences is correct?
    a. DNA - tRNA - mRNA - protein
    b. DNA - ribosome - mRNA - protein
    c. DNA - mRNA - tRNA - protein
    d. DNA - mRNA - rRNA - protein
    e. none of the above

Answer: c

37. The process of forming mRNA is called
    a. replication
    b. transcription
    c. translation
    d. ribolation
    e. protein synthesis

Answer: b

38. The stage in a cell's life cycle in which the cell performs its normal functions and prepares for division is called
    a. prophase
    b. metaphase
    c. interphase
    d. telophase
    e. anaphase

Answer: c

39. During the process of mitosis, chromatids separate into daughter chromosomes during
    a. prophase
    b. metaphase
    c. interphase
    d. telophase
    e. anaphase

Answer: e

40. During this phase of cell division, the nuclear membrane forms, the chromosomes uncoil, and cytokinesis may occur.
    a. anaphase
    b. prophase
    c. interphase
    d. telophase
    e. metaphase

Answer: d

41. During the process of mitosis, duplicated chromosomes line up along the equator of the cell during
    a. anaphase
    b. prophase
    c. interphase
    d. telophase
    e. metaphase

    Answer: e

42. The stage of mitosis at which chromosomes are first seen with the aid of a light microscope is
    a. anaphase
    b. prophase
    c. interphase
    d. telophase
    e. metaphase

    Answer: b

43. When genes are functionally eliminated, the cell loses its ability to create proteins. This specialization process is termed
    a. adaptation
    b. differentiation
    c. structural integration
    d. destabilization
    e. cellular activation

    Answer: b

44. Microvilli are found
    a. mostly in muscle cells.
    b. on the inside of cell membranes.
    c. in large numbers on cells that secrete hormones.
    d. in cells that are actively engaged in absorption.
    e. only on cells lining the reproductive tract.

    Answer: d

45. Hemolysis occurs when a blood cell is placed into
    a. isotonic solution
    b. hypertonic solution
    c. hypotonic solution
    d. holotonic solution
    e. none of the above

    Answer: c

46. The sodium-potassium exchange pump
    a. is an example of facilitated diffusion.
    b. does not require the input of cellular energy in the form of ATP.
    c. moves the sodium and potassium ions along their concentration gradients.
    d. is composed of a carrier protein located in the cell membrane.
    e. is not necessary for the maintenance of homeostasis.

Answer: d

47. Microfilaments
    a. are usually composed of myosin.
    b. are hollow, filamentous structures.
    c. anchor the cytoskeleton to integral proteins of the cell membrane.
    d. interact with filaments composed of tubulin to produce muscle contractions.
    e. are found in the cytoplasm radiating away from the centrosome.

Answer: c

48. If an animal cell lacked centrioles, it would not be able to
    a. move
    b. produce DNA
    c. divide
    d. synthesize proteins
    e. metabolize sugars

Answer: c

49. If a cell lacked ribosomes, it would not be able to
    a. move
    b. produce DNA
    c. divide
    d. synthesize proteins
    e. metabolize sugars

Answer: d

50. Following is a list of the steps involved in the process of secretion by the Golgi apparatus.
    1. material moves from saccule to saccule by means of transfer vesicles
    2. exocytosis
    3. products from RER are packaged into transport vesicles
    4. secretary vesicles are formed at the trans face
    5. vesicles arrive at the cis saccule
    6. enzymes modify arriving proteins and glycoproteins

    The proper sequence for these is

    a. 5, 6, 1, 4, 2, 3
    b. 2, 3, 5, 6, 1, 4
    c. 4, 3, 1, 6, 5, 2
    d. 3, 5, 6, 1, 4, 2
    e. 1, 3, 6, 4, 2, 5

    Answer: d

51. Two solutions are separated by a semipermeable membrane with the same properties as a cell membrane. Solution A is 5% glucose and solution B is 10% glucose. Under these circumstances
    a. water will move from solution A to solution B
    b. water will move from solution B to solution A
    c. glucose will move from solution A to solution B
    d. glucose will move from solution B to solution A
    e. at equilibrium the concentration of glucose will be higher in solution B

    Answer: a

52. If the amount of sodium ion in blood plasma increases
    a. the blood osmotic pressure will increase
    b. the blood osmotic pressure will decrease
    c. the blood osmotic pressure will stay the same
    d. the blood colloidal pressure will increase
    e. the blood colloidal pressure will decrease

    Answer: a

53. When sodium ion is moved across the cell membrane against its concentration gradient,
    a. diffusion occurs
    b. osmosis occurs
    c. cellular ATP is used
    d. vesicles are formed
    e. the cell membrane changes shape

    Answer: c

54. The mRNA sequence that is complementary to the sequence ATC on DNA would be
   a. ATC
   b. TAG
   c. UAG
   d. AUG
   e. none of the above

   Answer: c

55. The anticodon for the triplet UCA would be
   a. AGU
   b. AGC
   c. TCA
   d. TGT
   e. none of the above

   Answer: a

56. Examination of a sample of glandular cells reveals an extensive network of smooth endoplasmic reticulum. Which of the following would be a possible product of these cells?
   a. digestive enzymes
   b. steroid hormones
   c. protein hormones
   d. transport proteins
   e. antibodies

   Answer: b

57. The cell membrane:
   a. is a watery gel in which structures are suspended
   b. contains the power house of the cell
   c. is the central government of the cell
   d. protects the cell and acts as a filter
   e. carries the cell's hereditary information

   Answer: d

58. The rough endoplasmic reticulum:
   a. serves to increase the surface area of the cell
   b. contains bags of digestive juices
   c. assembles proteins for export
   d. is a network of channels for moving substances outside the cell
   e. is the same as cytosol

   Answer: c

59. Cellular organelles are located within the
    a. cytoplasm
    b. cell membrane
    c. phospholipid bilayer
    d. lipid droplets
    e. chromosomes

    Answer: a

60. The cellular organelle that is responsible for destroying foreign
    particles within the cell is:
    a. mitochondrium
    b. nucleus
    c. nucleolus
    d. Golgi bodies
    e. none of these

    Answer: d

61. The process that separates solid particles from liquids is known as:
    a. diffusion
    b. facilitated diffusion
    c. osmosis
    d. filtration
    e. active transport

    Answer: d

62. Vesicles are organelles that:
    a. produce ATP
    b. utilize ATP
    c. facilitate diffsuion
    d. temporarily store substances
    e. produce lysosomes

    Answer: d

63. Which process does **not** belong with the others in the following group?
    a. phagocytosis
    b. osmosis
    c. diffusion
    d. active transport
    e. exocytosis

    Answer: a

64. Osmosis **always** involves which of the following?
    a. sugar
    b. water
    c. salt
    d. carbohydrates
    e. proteins

    Answer: b

65. Which of these is an example of carrier-mediated transport?
    a. osmosis
    b. facilitated diffusion
    c. endocytosis
    d. exocytosis
    e. phagocytosis

    Answer: b

66. Identify the organelles that contain enzymes for the metabolism of hydrogen peroxide.
    a. lysosomes
    b. microvilli
    c. mitochondria
    d. nucleoli
    e. peroxisomes

    Answer: e

67. The class of membrane proteins that permits water and solutes to bypass the lipid portion of the cell membrane is:
    a. receptor proteins
    b. channel proteins
    c. carrier proteins
    d. anchor proteins
    e. identifier proteins

    Answer: b

68. Identify the phase of mitosis in which chromatin forms chromosomes.
    a. prophase
    b. metaphase
    c. anaphase
    d. telophase
    e. none of the above

    Answer: a

69. Identify the phase of mitosis in which the chromosomes elongate and the nuclear membranes form.
    a. prophase
    b. metaphase
    c. anaphase
    d. telophase
    e. none of the above

    Answer: d

70. Sex cells are produced by
    a. mitosis
    b. cytosis
    c. endocytosis
    d. phagocytosis
    e. meiosis

    Answer: e

71. The term "cancer" refers to:
    a. any of various malignant neoplasms
    b. neoplasms that have the tendency to metastasize to new sites
    c. an illness characterized by malignant cells
    d. all of the above
    e. none of the above

    Answer: d

72. Two types of RNA are:
    a. mRNA
    b. tRNA
    c. dRNA
    d. A and B
    e. B and C

    Answer: d

73. Which of the following consists of a network of intracellular membranes with attached ribosimes?
    a. rough ER
    b. smooth ER
    c. mitochondria
    d. nucleoli
    e. Golgi apparatus

    Answer: a

Fill-In-The-Blank

74. The theory that describes four basic concepts of cells is called _____ _____.

    Answer: cell theory

75. _____ proteins can open or close to regulate the passage of materials through the cell membrane.

    Answer: channel

76. The _____ of a membrane is the property that determines its effectiveness as a barrier.

    Answer: permeability

77. Cell membranes are said to be _____ permeable because they allow some substances to pass but not others.

    Answer: selectively

78. Membrane-bound proteins that allow recognition of a cell as "self" are called _____ proteins.

    Answer: identifier proteins

79. A(n) _____ _____ is a carrier system that moves one ion in one direction and another in the opposite direction.

    Answer: exchange pump

80. During active transport, a cell must expend _____ to accomplish the movement of a substance.

    Answer: energy

81. Movement of water from an area of high water concentration to an area of low water concentration is known as _____.

    Answer: osmosis

82. Osmotic pressure is determined by the _____ of solute molecules in a solution.

    Answer: number

83. Cilia are anchored to the cell by the structure called the _____ _____.

    Answer: basal body

84. The structure that allows locomotion in some cells is the _____.

    Answer: flagellum

85. The organelle that gives some endoplasmic reticula a "rough" appearance is the _____.

    Answer: ribosomes

86. Uncondensed genetic material is known as _____.

    Answer: chromatin

87. Ribosomes are composed of protein and _____.

    Answer: rRNA

88. The nucleus is surrounded by a membrane called the _____ _____.

    Answer: nuclear envelope

89. Communication between the nucleus and cytosol occurs through _____ _____.

    Answer: nuclear pores

90. One function of the nucleolus is to produce _____.

    Answer: ribosomes

91. A molecule of _____ consists of all the codons needed to produce a specific polypeptide chain.

    Answer: mRNA

92. The enzyme _____ is required for the synthesis of mRNA.

    Answer: RNA-polymerase

93. Amino acids are carried to the ribosomes to be incorporated into polypeptide chains by _____.

    Answer: tRNA

94. A triplet of nitrogenous bases on a tRNA molecule that interacts with the complementary codon on a mRNA strand is called a(n) _____.

Answer: anticodon

95. _____ are permanent alterations in a cell's DNA.

Answer: Mutations

96. In cells that are not dividing, chromosomes form a loose network of fibers known as _____.

Answer: chromatin

97. Cellular reproduction is known as _____.

Answer: cell division

98. _____ is the process of duplicating DNA prior to cell division.

Answer: Replication

99. The proper distribution of a cell's genetic material to two daughter cells is accomplished by the process of _____.

Answer: mitosis

100. The physical process by which a single animal cell separates into two cells is called _____.

Answer: cytokinesis

101. The process by which cells become specialized is called _____.

Answer: differentiation

102. A substance known to cause cancer is referred to as a(n) _____.

Answer: carcinogen

Essay

103. What is the benefit of having some of the cellular organelles enclosed by a membrane similar to the cell membrane?

    Answer:
    The isolation of the internal contents of membrane bound organelles allows them to manufacture or store secretions, enzymes, or toxins that could adversely affect the cytoplasm in general. Another benefit is the increased efficiency of having specialized enzyme systems concentrated in one place. For example, the concentration of enzymes necessary for energy production is in the mitochondrion.

104. When a person receives intravenous fluids to help build up blood volume, why is it important for the fluid to be isotonic?

    Answer:
    Intravenous fluids must be isotonic to prevent the cells from losing or gaining water. If the solution were hypertonic, the cells of the body would lose water, shrink, and possibly die. On the other hand, the introduction of hypotonic fluid would cause the cells to swell and possibly rupture.

105. Briefly explain the process of filtration as it relates to the function of kidneys.

    Answer:
    In filtration, hydrostatic pressure forces water across a membrane. The membrane serves as a barrier with holes of finite sizes to allow some substances to pass while retaining others. Substances such as sugars and proteins are too large to pass into the filtrate, so they remain in the blood. In cases of diseased physiological states, such as diabetes, these substances may not be retained and will pass into the urine.

Chapter 4:   The Tissue Level of Organization

Multiple Choice

1. Each of the following is a primary tissue type **except** one. Identify the exception.
   a. muscle tissue
   b. nervous tissue
   c. bone tissue
   d. connective tissue
   e. epithelial tissue

   Answer: c

2. Collections of specialized cells and cell products that perform a specific function are:
   a. cellular aggregates
   b. tissues
   c. organs
   d. organ systems
   e. cellular strata

   Answer: b

3. The tissue that always has a free surface exposed to the internal or external environment is
   a. epithelial tissue
   b. connective tissue
   c. muscle tissue
   d. nervous tissue
   e. contractive tissue

   Answer: a

4. Epithelial cells are adapted for
   a. contraction
   b. conduction
   c. secretion
   d. circulation
   e. support

   Answer: c

5. Epithelial cells that are adapted for absorption or secretion usually have _____ at their free surface.
   a. many mitochondria
   b. cilia
   c. microvilli
   d. Golgi complexes
   e. junctional complexes

   Answer: c

6. A type of intercellular connection in which the outermost lipid portions of the two cell membranes is fused is termed a(n):
   a. tight junction
   b. gap junction
   c. intermediate junction
   d. desmosome
   e. none of the above

   Answer: a

7. Dead skin cells are shed in thick sheets because the strong links are held together by _____.
   a. gap junctions
   b. intermediate junctions
   c. tight junctions
   d. desmosomes
   e. junctional complexes

   Answer: d

8. Epithelium is connected to underlying connective tissue by
   a. a basement membrane
   b. junctional complexes
   c. intercellular glue
   d. a fibrous netting
   e. reticular fibers

   Answer: a

9. The basic shapes of epithelial cells include all **but** which of the following?
   a. stratified
   b. squamous
   c. cuboidal
   d. columnar
   e. all of the above are correct

   Answer: a

10. The type of epithelium that is found lining internal body compartments and blood vessels is
    a. simple squamous
    b. stratified squamous
    c. simple cuboidal
    d. stratified cuboidal
    e. transitional

    Answer: a

11. Which of the following is **not** a correct statement about simple epithelia?
    a. They afford little mechanical protection.
    b. They are characteristic of regions where secretion or absorption occurs.
    c. They line internal compartments and passageways.
    d. They cover surfaces subjected to mechanical or chemical stress.
    e. They are avascular.

Answer: d

12. The type of epithelium found where absorption or secretion takes place is
    a. simple squamous
    b. simple cuboidal
    c. stratified squamous
    d. transitional
    e. pseudostratified columnar

Answer: b

13. Simple cuboidal epithelium would be found
    a. at the surface of the skin
    b. lining the trachea
    c. lining blood vessels
    d. lining the chambers of the thyroid gland
    e. lining the air sacs of the lungs

Answer: d

14. A transitional epithelium would be found
    a. lining the urinary bladder
    b. lining the ducts that drain sweat glands
    c. lining kidney tubules
    d. lining the stomach
    e. at the surface of the skin

Answer: a

15. One would find pseudostratified columnar epithelium lining the
    a. trachea
    b. urinary bladder
    c. heart
    d. surface of the skin
    e. stomach

Answer: a

16. Which of the following is a type of secretion in which some cytoplasm is lost with the product?
    a. holocrine
    b. merocrine
    c. apocrine
    d. mucous
    e. none of the above

    Answer: c

17. Functions of connective tissue include
    a. establishing a structural framework for the body
    b. transporting fluids and dissolved materials
    c. providing protection for delicate organs
    d. storing energy reserves
    e. all of the above

    Answer: e

18. The fibrous components of connective tissue are produced by
    a. fibroblasts
    b. adipocytes
    c. macrophages
    d. mast cells
    e. melanocytes

    Answer: a

19. Cells that store fat are called
    a. fibroblasts
    b. macrophages
    c. adipocytes
    d. mast cells
    e. melanocytes

    Answer: c

20. Loose connective tissue functions in
    a. filling spaces between organs
    b. supporting epithelia and anchoring blood vessels
    c. storing starch and lipids
    d. a and b only
    e. none of the above

    Answer: d

21. The dominant fiber type in dense connective tissue is
    a. collagen
    b. elastin
    c. actin
    d. myosin
    e. fibrin

    Answer: a

22. The cell that accounts for almost half the volume of blood is the
    a. erythrocyte
    b. leukocyte
    c. platelet
    d. phagocyte
    e. none of the above

    Answer: a

23. Chondrocytes are to cartilage as osteocytes are to
    a. blood
    b. fat
    c. epithelium
    d. bone
    e. nervous tissue

    Answer: d

24. The most common type of cartilage is
    a. ligamentous
    b. hyaline
    c. elastic
    d. fibrocartilage
    e. osseous

    Answer: b

25. Which of the following lines cavities that communicate with the exterior of the body?
    a. mucous membranes
    b. serous membranes
    c. cutaneous membranes
    d. synovial membranes
    e. pleural membranes

    Answer: a

26. The reduction of friction between the parietal and visceral surfaces of an internal cavity is the function of
    a. cutaneous membranes
    b. mucous membranes
    c. serous membranes
    d. synovial membranes
    e. the skin

    Answer: c

27. The serous membrane lining the abdominal cavity is the
    a. pleura
    b. peritoneum
    c. pericardium
    d. perichondrium
    e. periosteum

    Answer: b

28. Tissue that is specialized for contraction is
    a. cartilage
    b. nerve tissue
    c. epithelium
    d. connective tissue
    e. muscle

    Answer: e

29. The muscle tissue which shows no striations is
    a. skeletal muscle
    b. smooth muscle
    c. cardiac muscle
    d. voluntary muscle
    e. multinucleated muscle

    Answer: b

30. The muscle tissue that is generally multinucleate is
    a. skeletal muscle
    b. smooth muscle
    c. cardiac muscle
    d. voluntary muscle
    e. multinucleate muscle

    Answer: a

31. The muscle that is located in the walls of hollow internal organs is
    a. skeletal muscle
    b. smooth muscle
    c. cardiac muscle
    d. voluntary muscle
    e. multinucleate muscle

Answer: b

32. Tissue that is specialized for the conduction of electrical impulses is called
    a. muscle tissue
    b. nervous tissue
    c. areolar tissue
    d. osseous tissue
    e. epithelial tissue

Answer: b

33. The neuron is made up of all of the following **except**
    a. a soma
    b. dendrites
    c. an axon
    d. nerve fibers
    e. a synapse

Answer: e

34. An inflammation resulting from a pathogen is known as a(n)
    a. invasion
    b. neoplasm
    c. infection
    d. cancer
    e. none of the above

Answer: c

35. Inflammation at an injury site produces which of the following responses?
    a. redness, warmth and swelling
    b. bleeding, clotting and hemolysis
    c. necrosis, fibrosis and scarring
    d. hematoma, shivering and fever
    e. none of the above are correct

Answer: a

36. Tissue changes with age include
    a. less efficient tissue maintenance
    b. decreased ability to repair and more fragile connective tissue
    c. thicker epithelium
    d. a and b only
    e. none of the above

    Answer: d

37. Tissue changes with age can be the result of
    a. hormonal changes
    b. changes in lifestyle
    c. improper nutrition
    d. inadequate levels of activity
    e. all of the above

    Answer: e

38. Examination of a tubular structure with the electron microscope reveals a lining of cells with stereocilia. This tissue is from
    a. the stomach
    b. the small intestine
    c. the female reproductive system
    d. the male reproductive system
    e. the urinary bladder

    Answer: d

39. Perspiration is an example of what type of secretion?
    a. merocrine
    b. holocrine
    c. apocrine
    d. serous
    e. endocrine

    Answer: a

40. Cells that remove damaged cells or pathogens from connective tissue are
    a. fibroblasts
    b. adipocytes
    c. melanocytes
    d. macrophages
    e. mast cells

    Answer: d

41. Why does damaged cartilage heal slowly?
    a. Chondrocytes cannot be replaced if killed, and other cell types must take their place.
    b. Cartilage is avascular so nutrients and other molecules must diffuse to the site of injury.
    c. Damaged cartilage becomes calcified, thus blocking the movement of materials required for healing.
    d. Chondrocytes divide more slowly than other cell types, delaying the healing process.
    e. Damaged collagen cannot be quickly replaced, thus slowing the healing process.

    Answer: b

42. Unlike cartilage, bone
    a. is a connective tissue.
    b. has a matrix that contains collagen.
    c. is very vascular.
    d. has a two-layered outer covering.
    e. has cells that are located in spaces called lacunae.

    Answer: c

43. Cardiac muscle differs from the other two types of muscle tissue in that cardiac muscle
    a. has visible striations.
    b. has only one nucleus per cell.
    c. has the ability to contract independent of neural stimulation.
    d. contains actin and myosin filaments.
    e. forms muscle fibers.

    Answer: c

44. Close examination of an organ reveals a lining of several layers of cells. The layers do not contain any blood vessels and one surface of the cells is open to the internal cavity of the organ. This tissue is probably
    a. epithelium
    b. muscle
    c. nervous
    d. connective tissue
    e. fat tissue

    Answer: a

45. Examination of a tissue sample reveals groups of cells united by junctional complexes and interlocking membranes. The cells have one free surface and lack blood vessels. The tissue is most likely
    a. muscle
    b. nervous
    c. epithelium
    d. connective tissue
    e. adipose tissue

    Answer: c

46. Types of epithelial tissue include all of the following **except**:
    a. cartilage
    b. simple squamous
    c. glandular
    d. pseudostratified columnar
    e. transitional

    Answer: a

47. Types of muscle tissue include:
    a. skeletal, smooth, and fibrous
    b. simple squamous, adipose, and smooth
    c. skeletal, smooth, and cardiac
    d. bone, elastic connective, and simple columnar
    e. fibrous connective, stratified squamous, and skeletal

    Answer: c

48. Cells of similar structure and function are organized into groups called
    a. organs
    b. tendons
    c. tissues
    d. cartilage
    e. nerves

    Answer: c

49. Examples of fibrous connective tissue include:
    a. tendons
    b. salivary glands
    c. respiratory passages
    d. ligaments
    e. A and D

    Answer: e

50. The function of epithelial tissue is to
    a. provide physical protection
    b. control permeability
    c. provide sensations
    d. produce specialized secretions
    e. all of the above

    Answer: e

51. The urinary bladder and renal pelvic have this type of tissue:
    a. simple squamous
    b. stratified squamous
    c. transitional epithelium
    d. pseudostratified columnar epithelium
    e. simple cuboidal

    Answer: c

52. The alveoli of the lungs are made of:
    a. stratified squamous
    b. columnar
    c. transitional epithelia
    d. simple squamous
    e. transitional epithelia

    Answer: b

53. Another name for the skin is the
    a. mucous membrane
    b. synovial membrane
    c. serous membrane
    d. glandular membrane
    e. cutaneous membrane

    Answer: e

54. The functions of connective tissues include:
    a. support
    b. protection
    c. storage of adipose
    d. all of the above
    e. none of the above

    Answer: d

55. This type of tissue is specialized to conduct electrical impulses throughout the body:
    a. neural
    b. cardiac
    c. skeletal
    d. serous
    e. reticular

    Answer: a

56. Which lacks a direct blood supply?
    a. cartilage
    b. bone
    c. muscle
    d. nerves
    e. skin

    Answer: a

57. The four main types of tissues include:
    a. epithelium
    b. muscle
    c. nerve
    d. connective
    e. all of the above

    Answer: e

58. The most widely dispersed type of tissue in the human body is:
    a. connective
    b. epithelial
    c. muscle
    d. nerve
    e. squamous

    Answer: a

59. Another term for skeletal muscle tissue is:
    a. involuntary
    b. smooth voluntary
    c. striated voluntary
    d. smooth
    e. cardiac

    Answer: c

60. Another term for cardiac muscle tissue is:
   a. striated involuntary
   b. striated voluntary
   c. smooth involuntary
   d. smooth voluntary
   e. neural tissue

   Answer: a

61. Another term for smooth muscle tissue is:
   a. striated involuntary
   b. smooth voluntary
   c. non-striated involuntary
   d. cardiac
   e. striated voluntary

   Answer: c

62. With age, tissues:
   a. grow less efficient
   b. have altered chemical composition
   c. are more efficient
   d. A and B
   e. A and C

   Answer: d

63. Approximately seventy-five percent of cancers in the aging population are the result of:
   a. inadequate diets
   b. chemical exposures
   c. environmental factors
   d. A and B
   e. B and C

   Answer: e

Fill-In-The-Blank

64. The study of tissue is called _____.

   Answer: histoloty

65. Secretions onto body surfaces are characteristic of _____ glands.

   Answer: exocrine

66. Secretions directly into the blood are characteristic of _____ glands.

   Answer: endocrine

67. Unspecialized epithelial cells which act as a source for mitosis are called _____ cells.

    Answer: stem

68. The study of epithelial cells shed and collected at the epithelial surface is _____ cytology.

    Answer: exfoliative

69. _____ _____ is the fluid component of connective tissue.

    Answer: Ground substance

70. The combination of fibers and ground substance in supporting connective tissues is known as _____.

    Answer: matrix

71. The watery ground substance of blood is called _____.

    Answer: plasma

72. Epithelial and connective tissues combine to form _____ and tissues in the body.

    Answer: membranes

73. _____ membranes are associated with body cavities that lack openings to the outside.

    Answer: Serous

74. _____ membranes are associated with freely-moveable joints.

    Answer: Synovial

75. _____ are cells that are modified to transmit signals from one place to another.

    Answer: Neurons

76. _____ are cells that support and protect the neurons.

    Answer: Neuroglia (Glia)

77. The body's first response to any injury is termed _____.

    Answer: inflammation

78. The process of tissue replacement is called _____.

Answer: regeneration

79. _____ are physicians who specialize in the identification and treatment of cancers.

Answer: Oncologists

80. Regions where adjacent cardiocytes interlock and electrical coupling between cells occurs are _____ _____.

Answer: intercalated disks

Essay → Group Work

81. What type of epithelium would you expect to find lining the alveoli (air sacs) in the lungs?

Answer:
Since air must diffuse from the alveoli into the bloodstream, you would expect to find very thin cells, or squamous epithelium. Thicker types of epithelial cells would slow the process of gas diffusion to and from the blood.

82. During a lab practical, a student examines a tissue that is composed of densely packed protein fibers that are running parallel forming a cord. There are no nuclei or striations, and there is no evidence of other cellular structures. The student identifies the tissue as skeletal muscle. Why is the student's choice wrong, and what tissue is s/he probably observing?

Answer:
Skeletal muscle tissue would be made up of densely packed fibers running in the same direction, but since these fibers are composed of cells they would have many nuclei and mitochondria. Skeletal muscle also has an obvious banding pattern or striations due to the arrangement of the actin and myosin filaments within the cell. The student is probably looking at a slide of tendon (dense connective tissue).

83. Analysis of a glandular secretion indicates that it contains some DNA, RNA, and membrane components such as phospholipids. What kind of secretion is this and why?

Answer:
The presence of DNA, RNA, and membrane components suggests that the cell was destroyed during the process of secretion. This is consistent with a holocrine type of secretion.

84. While in the chemistry lab, Jim accidentally spills a small amount of a caustic chemical on his arm. What changes in the characteristics of the skin would you expect to observe and what would cause these changes?

Answer:
You would expect the skin in the area to become red and warm. It would also swell and Jim would experience a painful sensation. These changes occur as a result of the inflammation reaction, the body's first response to injury. Injury to the epithelium and underlying connective tissue would trigger the release of chemicals from specialized inflammatory cells in the area. These chemicals in turn initiate the changes that are observed.

Chapter 5:   The Integumentary System

Multiple Choice

1. Each of the following is a function of the integumentary system **except** one. Identify the exception.
   a. protection of underlying tissue
   b. excretion
   c. maintenance of body temperature
   d. synthesis of vitamin C
   e. nutrition and storage

   Answer: d

2. The two components of the cutaneous membrane are the
   a. epidermis and dermis
   b. epidermis and subcutaneous layer
   c. dermis and subcutaneous layer
   d. integument and dermis
   e. epidermis and superficial fascia

   Answer: a

3. Accessory structures of the skin include
   a. hair follicles
   b. sebaceous and sweat glands
   c. nails
   d. a and b only
   e. all of the above

   Answer: e

4. The layer of the epidermis that contains cells undergoing division is the
   a. stratum corneum
   b. stratum lucidum
   c. stratum germinativum
   d. stratum granulosum
   e. stratum spinosum

   Answer: c

5. An epidermal layer found only in the skin of the palms of the hands and the soles of the feet is the
   a. stratum corneum
   b. stratum lucidum
   c. stratum germinativum
   d. stratum granulosum
   e. stratum spinosum

   Answer: b

6. The layer of the epidermis that contains melanocytes is the
   a. stratum corneum
   b. stratum lucidum
   c. stratum germinativum
   d. stratum granulosum
   e. stratum spinosum

Answer: c

7. An albino individual lacks the ability to produce
   a. melanin
   b. keratin
   c. carotene
   d. keratinocytes
   e. collgen

Answer: a

8. Perspiration produced by merocrine sweat glands
   a. is more than 99% water
   b. contains electrolytes and waste products
   c. helps to cool the body when it evaporates
   d. helps to prevent bacteria from colonizing the skin
   e. all of the above

Answer: e

9. Sweat tastes salty because of its
   a. water
   b. metabolites
   c. waste products
   d. electrolytes
   e. acidic pH

Answer: d

10. The pigment melanin
    a. is produced by cells called melanocytes and is found in higher
       concentration in individuals with darker skin
    b. is usually some shade of red, yellow or brown
    c. protects DNA from the damaging effects of U.V. radiation
    d. a and c only
    e. all of the above

Answer: d

11. Exposure of the skin to ultraviolet light
    a. can result in increased numbers of melanocytes forming in the skin
    b. can result in decreased melanin production by melanocytes
    c. can cause destruction of vitamin D
    d. can result in damage to the DNA of cells in the stratum germinativum
    e. has no effect on the skin cells

    Answer: d

12. The layer of the skin that contains the blood vessels and nerves that supply the surface of the skin is the
    a. papillary layer
    b. reticular layer
    c. epidermal layer
    d. subcutaneous layer
    e. hypodermal layer

    Answer: a

13. Glands that discharge a waxy secretion into hair follicles are
    a. ceruminous glands
    b. apocrine sweat glands
    c. sebaceous glands
    d. merocrine sweat glands
    e. mammary glands

    Answer: c

14. Most body odor is the result of bacterial metabolism of the secretions produced by
    a. ceruminous glands
    b. apocrine sweat glands
    c. sebaceous glands
    d. merocrine sweat glands
    e. mammary glands

    Answer: b

15. The highest concentration of merocrine sweat glands would be found
    a. in the axillae
    b. on the chest
    c. on the palms of the hands
    d. on the back
    e. surrounding the genitals

    Answer: c

16. The nail body covers the
    a. nail root
    b. nail bed
    c. lunula
    d. free edge
    e. cuticle

    Answer: b

17. Nail production occurs at the
    a. body
    b. bed
    c. root
    d. cuticle
    e. free edge

    Answer: c

18. The dense mass of dead, keratinized cells of the nail is the
    a. body
    b. bed
    c. root
    d. cuticle
    e. free edge

    Answer: a

19. The condition that results from clogged sebaceous glands is
    a. a boil
    b. a carbuncle
    c. acne
    d. a blister
    e. none of the above

    Answer: c

20. Variations in hair color reflect differences in the type and amount of pigment produced by
    a. keratinocytes
    b. melanocytes
    c. dermal papillae
    d. carotene cells
    e. the papillary layer of the dermis

    Answer: b

21. Differences in hair appearance results from which of the following?
    a. size of the follicle
    b. shape of the follicle
    c. amount of melanin in the keratinized epidermis of the hair shaft
    d. activity of the follicle cells
    e. all of the above are correct

    Answer: e

22. A "rug burn" is an example of a(n):
    a. abrasion
    b. laceration
    c. puncture
    d. incision
    e. contusion

    Answer: a

23. The layer of the skin that provides protection against bacteria as well
    as chemical and mechanical injuries is the
    a. dermis
    b. subcutaneous layer
    c. epidermis
    d. papillary layer
    e. sebum layer

    Answer: c

24. The repair of the dermis begins as fibroblasts produce
    a. elastic fibers
    b. collagen fibers
    c. reticular fibers
    d. dense connective tissue
    e. periosteum

    Answer: b

25. The effects of aging on the skin include
    a. a decline in the activity of sebaceous glands
    b. increased production of vitamin D
    c. thickening of the epidermis
    d. an increased blood supply to the dermis
    e. an increased number of sweat glands

    Answer: a

26. Thick skin can be found on the _____.
    a. back
    b. palms
    c. legs
    d. arms
    e. chest

    Answer: b

27. Epidermal ridges
    a. extend into the dermis
    b. interconnect with the dermal papillae
    c. cause ridge patterns on the surface of the skin
    d. produce patterns that are determined genetically
    e. all of the above

    Answer: e

28. _____ are macrophages in the epidermis that are part of the immune system.
    a. Langerhan's cells
    b. Merkel cells
    c. Melanocytes
    d. Basal cells
    e. Squamous cells

    Answer: a

29. An important vitamin that is formed in the skin when it is exposed to sunlight is
    a. vitamin A
    b. vitamin B
    c. vitamin C
    d. vitamin D
    e. vitamin E

    Answer: d

30. When the arrector pili muscles contract
    a. "goose bumps" are formed
    b. hairs are shed
    c. sweat is released from sweat glands
    d. shivering occurs
    e. the skin changes color

    Answer: a

31. Deodorants are used to mask the odor of _____ secretions.
    a. sebaceous
    b. apocrine
    c. merocrine
    d. mammary
    e. ceruminous

Answer: b

32. The type of burn that may require a skin graft is a
    a. first degree
    b. second degree
    c. third degree burn
    d. partial thickness burn
    e. all of the above are correct

Answer: c

33. When a fair-skinned person blushes, why does his or her skin turn red?
    a. The blood supply to the skin increases.
    b. The number of red melanocytes in the skin increases.
    c. Melanocytes increase production of red pigments.
    d. The blood supply to the skin decreases.
    e. Increased heat causes the skin to turn red.

Answer: a

34. Stretch marks occur when
    a. the skin is stretched in normal movements
    b. surgical incisions are made perpendicular to the skin's lines of
       cleavage
    c. the skin is so extensively stretched that its elastic capabilities
       are exceeded
    d. athletes overextend a muscle
    e. the hair follicles cease to produce hairs

Answer: c

35. In order for bacteria on the skin to cause an infection in the skin,
    they must
    a. survive the bactericidal components of sebum
    b. avoid being flushed from the surface of the skin by sweat
    c. penetrate the stratum corneum
    d. escape the Langerhan's cells
    e. all of the above

Answer: e

36. Skin can regenerate effectively even after considerable damage has occurred because
    a. the epidermis of the skin has a rich supply of small blood vessels
    b. stem cells persist in both the epithelial and connective tissue components of the skin even after injury
    c. fibroblasts in the dermis can give rise to new germinal cells in the epidermis
    d. contraction in the area of the injury brings cells of adjacent strata together
    e. cells of the stratum germinativum cannot migrate to other positions in the skin

    Answer: b

37. Scar tissue is the result of
    a. an abnormally large number of collagen fibers and relatively few blood vessels at the repair site
    b. increased numbers of epidermal layers in the area of the injury
    c. a thickened stratum germinativum in the area of the injury
    d. increased numbers of fibroblasts and mast cells in the injured area
    e. a lack of hair follicles and sebaceous glands in the injured area

    Answer: a

38. Wrinkles and sagging skin in elderly individuals are the result of
    a. increased production of epidermis
    b. thinning of the epidermis and loss of the protein elastin
    c. increased keratinization of the epidermis
    d. the loss of glands and hair follicles from the skin
    e. decreased thickness of the dermis

    Answer: b

39. Why would an elderly person be more prone to skin infections than a younger person?
    a. Skin repairs take longer in the elderly.
    b. The epidermis is thinner in the elderly.
    c. There are fewer Langerhan's cells in the skin of the elderly.
    d. The blood supply to the dermis is reduced in the skin of the elderly.
    e. all of the above

    Answer: e

40. The reproducing cells of the skin are located in the:
    a. surface
    b. stratum corneum
    c. stratum lucidum
    d. stratum germinativum
    e. stratum spinosum

    Answer: c

41. The pigment responsible for giving skin its hue is:
    a. melanin
    b. keratin
    c. carotene
    d. biliverdin
    e. bilirubin

    Answer: a

42. Accessory structures of the skin include:
    a. hair follicles
    b. arrector pili muscles
    c. sebaceous glands
    d. apocrine sweat glands
    e. all of the above

    Answer: e

43. Hair is composed of
    a. discharge from sebaceous glands
    b. dead keratinized cells
    c. reticular tissue
    d. epidermal ridges
    e. the hypodermis

    Answer: b

44. Epidermal cells synthesize this vitamin when exposed to sunlight.
    a. vitamin D2
    b. vitamin C
    c. vitamin E
    d. vitamin D3
    e. vitamin A

    Answer: d

45. The glands that are sensitive to changes in sex hormone concentrations
    are
    a. sweat glands
    b. integumentary glands
    c. sebaceous glands
    d. dermal glands
    e. merocrine glands

    Answer: c

46. The most numerous glands are the _____ glands.
    a. merocrine
    b. apocrine
    c. sebaceous
    d. salivary
    e. endrocrine

    Answer: a

47. When the skin is exposed to ultraviolet radiation, it responds by
    a. decreasing melanin production
    b. increasing heart rate
    c. decreasing carotene production
    d. increasing melanin production
    e. increasing carotene production

    Answer: d

48. Drugs suspended in _____ or _____ can penetrate the epidermis.
    a. water; blood
    b. water; lipids
    c. oils; alcohol
    d. oils; lipid-soluble carriers
    e. sebum; water

    Answer: d

49. Skin color is the result of
    a. pigment concentration
    b. dermal blood supply
    c. pigment composition
    d. number of keratinocytes
    e. A, B, and C

    Answer: e

50. Temporary increases in hair loss can result from
    a. drugs
    b. dietary factors
    c. radiation
    d. fever
    e. all of the above

    Answer: e

51. This type of burn appears inflamed and tender, but has no blisters.
    a. first-degree burn
    b. second-degree burn
    c. third-degree burn
    d. full-thickness burn
    e. none of the above

    Answer: a

52. Integumentary changes associated with the aging process include all of the following **except**:
    a. increased muscle strength
    b. reduction of the immune response
    c. decreased repair process
    d. decreased ability to maintain body temperature
    e. decreased glandular activity

    Answer: a

53. The condition resulting from blocked sebaceous ducts is known as
    a. seborrhea
    b. dermatitis
    c. acne
    d. dandruff
    e. psoriasis

    Answer: c

Fill-In-The-Blank

54. The _____ layer of the skin contains bundles of collagen fibers and elastin and is responsible for the strength of the skin.

    Answer: reticular

55. The structure that connects epithelium with underlying connective tissue is the _____ _____.

    Answer: basement membrane

56. The substance which gives the skin its waterproofing ability is _____.

    Answer: keratin

57. In the condition known as cyanosis, the skin takes on a _____ color.

    Answer: blue

58. _____ is a pigment found in vegetables that can make skin appear orange or yellow.

    Answer: Carotene

59. The main function of the sweat glands is to _____ body temperature by producing sweat

    Answer: decrease (lower)

60. Exposure to _____ radiation from the sun has the effect of increasing melanin production in the skin.

    Answer: ultraviolet (U.V.)

61. The waxy substance produced to keep skin and hair from cracking and drying out is _____.

    Answer: sebum

62. The nail _____ covers the nail bed.

    Answer: body

63. Hairs originate in structures called _____ _____.

    Answer: hair follicles

64. A thickened area of scar tissue that is covered by a shiny, smooth epidermal surface is called a(n) _____.

    Answer: keloid

65. A fibrin clot that is formed at the surface of the skin is called a(n) _____.

    Answer: scab

66. _____ are accumulations of fluid within the epidermis or between the epidermis and the dermis.

    Answer: Blisters

Essay

67. In a condition known as sunstroke, the victim appears flushed, the skin is warm and dry, and the body temperature rises dramatically. Explain these observations based on what you know concerning the role of the skin in thermoregulation.

Answer:
When the body temperature increases, more blood flow is directed to the vessels of the skin. The red pigment in the blood gives the skin a redder than usual color and accounts for the victim's flushed appearance. The skin is dry because the sweat glands are not producing sweat (to avoid further dehydration). Without evaporation cooling, not enough heat is dissipated from the skin, the skin is warm, and the body temperature rises.

68. Two patients are brought to the emergency room. One has cut his finger with a knife; the other has stepped on a nail. Which wound has a greater chance of becoming infected? Why?

Answer:
The puncture wound has a greater chance of becoming infected than the knife cut because the cut from the knife will bleed freely, washing away many of the bacteria from the wound site. In a puncture wound, bacteria can be forced beneath the surface of the skin and past the skin's protective barriers, thus increasing the possibility of infection.

69. Many medications can be administered transdermally by applying patches that contain the medication to the surface of the skin. These patches can be attached anywhere on the skin except the palms of the hands and the soles of the feet. Why?

Answer:
The palms of the hands and the soles of the feet have an extra layer in the epidermis, the stratum lucidum. The presence of this extra layer slows down the rate of diffusion of the medication and significantly decreases its effectiveness.

Chapter 6:   Osseous Tissue and Skeletal Structure

Multiple Choice

1. Functions of the skeletal system include
   a. support
   b. storage
   c. protection
   d. blood cell production
   e. all of the above

   Answer: e

2. Mature bone cells are termed
   a. osteocytes
   b. osteoblasts
   c. osteoclasts
   d. chondrocytes
   e. osteons

   Answer: a

3. Cells that synthesize the organic components of the bone matrix are termed
   a. osteocytes
   b. stem cells
   c. osteoblasts
   d. osteoclasts
   e. chondrocytes

   Answer: c

4. Large, multinucleated cells that can dissolve the bony matrix are termed
   a. osteocytes
   b. stem cells
   c. osteoblasts
   d. osteoclasts
   e. chondrocytes

   Answer: d

5. The narrow passageways that contain cytoplasmic extensions of osteocytes are termed
   a. lamellae
   b. lacunae
   c. canaliculi
   d. marrow cavities
   e. matrices

   Answer: c

6. The basic functional unit of compact bone is the
   a. osteocyte
   b. osteoclast
   c. osteon
   d. oseous matrix
   e. osseous lamellae

   Answer: c

7. The plates of bone found in spongy bone are called
   a. osteons
   b. trabeculae
   c. concentric lamellae
   d. interstitial lamellae
   e. lacunae

   Answer: b

8. The medullary cavity of bones contains
   a. compact bone
   b. osteons
   c. cartilage
   d. marrow
   e. periosteum

   Answer: d

9. The shaft of a long bone is called the
   a. epiphysis
   b. diaphysis
   c. osteon
   d. epiphyseal plate
   e. lamella

   Answer: b

10. The lining of the marrow cavity is called the
    a. endosteum
    b. periosteum
    c. epimysium
    d. perimysium
    e. none of the above

    Answer: a

11. In intramembranous ossification
    a. osteoblasts differentiate within a connective tissue
    b. osteoblasts cluster together to form compact bone in locations called ossification centers
    c. small struts of bone called spicules radiate out from the ossification centers to join with neighboring spicules
    d. a and c only
    e. all of the above

Answer: d

12. Endochondral ossification begins with the formation of
    a. a fibrous connective tissue model
    b. a cartilaginous model
    c. a membranous model
    d. a calcified model
    e. no model at all, just the presence of osteoblasts

Answer: b

13. The following are major steps in the process of endochondral ossification
    1. blood vessels invade the perichondrium
    2. osteoclasts create a marrow cavity
    3. chondrocytes enlarge and calcify
    4. osteoblasts replace calcified cartilage with spongy bone
    5. the perichondrium is converted into periosteum and the inner layer produces bone

    The correct order for these events is
    a. 3, 1, 5, 4, 2
    b. 1, 3, 5, 4, 2
    c. 1, 5, 3, 4, 2
    d. 2, 3, 1, 5, 4
    e. 3, 1, 4, 5, 2

Answer: a

14. Secondary ossification centers occur
    a. in the medullary cavity of the diaphysis
    b. at the outer surface of the diaphysis
    c. in the center of the epiphyses
    d. at the surface of the epiphyses
    e. in the dermis of the skin

Answer: c

15. When sexual hormone production increases, bone growth
    a. slows down
    b. accelerates rapidly
    c. increases slowly
    d. increases, but only in thickness
    e. is not affected

    Answer: b

16. The presence of an epiphyseal line indicates
    a. epiphyseal growth has ended
    b. epiphyseal growth is just beginning
    c. growth in bone diameter is just beginning
    d. the bone is fractured at that location
    e. the presence of an epiphyseal line does not indicate any particular event

    Answer: a

17. The most abundant mineral in the human body is
    a. sodium
    b. potassium
    c. phosphorus
    d. calcium
    e. sulfur

    Answer: d

18. Elevated levels of calcium ion in the blood stimulate the secretion of the hormone
    a. calcitonin
    b. thyroid hormone
    c. parathyroid hormone
    d. growth hormone
    e. testosterone

    Answer: a

19. The hormone calcitonin functions to
    a. stimulate osteoclast activity
    b. decrease the rate of calcium excretion
    c. increase the rate of bone deposition
    d. decrease the level of calcium ion in the blood
    e. all of the above

    Answer: c

20. The parathyroid hormone
    a. stimulates osteoclast activity
    b. increases the rate of calcium absorption
    c. decreases the rate of calcium excretion
    d. a and c only
    e. all of the above

    Answer: e

21. Factors that are necessary for proper bone formation include
    a. vitamins A and C
    b. vitamin E and B12
    c. the hormone thyroxine
    d. a and c only
    e. all of the above

    Answer: d

22. Vitamin D is necessary for
    a. collagen formation
    b. absorption and transport of calcium and phosphate ions
    c. reducing osteoblast activity
    d. increasing osteoclast activity
    e. the formation of the organic framework of bone

    Answer: b

23. A lack of exercise would
    a. cause bones to become thicker
    b. cause bones to store more calcium
    c. result in thin, brittle bones
    d. increase the length of a bone
    e. have no effect on a bone

    Answer: c

24. When stress is applied to a bone
    a. osteoblast activity increases
    b. osteoclast activity increases
    c. it becomes thin and brittle
    d. it bends
    e. trabeculae are formed perpendicular to the zone of stress to increase
       strength

    Answer: a

25. The normal loss of bone that occurs with aging is called
    a. osteopenia
    b. osteoporosis
    c. osteogenesis
    d. osteoinflammation
    e. bone cancer

    Answer: a

26. A large rough projection of a bone (found only on the femur) is termed a
    a. wall
    b. trochanter
    c. tuberosity
    d. tubercle
    e. condyle

    Answer: b

27. A small round projection of a bone is termed a
    a. wall
    b. trochanter
    c. tuberosity
    d. tubercle
    e. facet

    Answer: d

28. The smooth, rounded or oval articular process of a bone is termed a
    a. crest
    b. ridge
    c. head
    d. condyle
    e. trochlea

    Answer: d

29. A shallow depression on a bone is termed a
    a. fossa
    b. sulcus
    c. facet
    d. fissure
    e. line

    Answer: a

30. A passageway through bone is termed a
    a. sinus
    b. meatus
    c. fissure
    d. foramen
    e. fossa

    Answer: b

31. Which of the following is **not** a part of the axial division of the skeletal system?
    a. skull
    b. auditory ossicles
    c. hyoid bone
    d. pectoral girdle
    e. vertebral column

    Answer: d

32. Which of the following is a function of the axial skeleton?
    a. support and protect organs in the dorsal and ventral body cavities
    b. provide an attachment for muscles that move the head, neck, and trunk
    c. provide an attachment for muscles involved in respiration
    d. a and c only
    e. all of the above

    Answer: e

33. A landmark found near the proximal end of the humerus would be the
    a. medial epicondyle
    b. lateral epicondyle
    c. greater tubercle
    d. olecranon fossa
    e. capitulum

    Answer: c

34. The appendicular skeleton consists of
    a. the bones of the arms
    b. the bones of the legs
    c. the bones of the hands and feet
    d. the bones that connect the limbs to the axial skeleton
    e. all of the above

    Answer: e

35. Which of the following is **not** a component of the appendicular skeleton?
    a. scapula
    b. hyoid
    c. femur
    d. humerus
    e. coxa

    Answer: b

36. The depression on the anterior surface at the distal end of the humerus is the
    a. olecranon fossa
    b. coronoid fossa
    c. radial fossa
    d. greater tubercle
    e. radial groove

    Answer: b

37. The bones of the forearm include the
    a. humerus
    b. femur
    c. tibia
    d. fibula
    e. radius

    Answer: e

38. The olecranon process would be found on the
    a. humerus
    b. radius
    c. ulna
    d. femur
    e. tibia

    Answer: c

39. The elevation that extends along the lateral border of the shaft of the humerus is the
    a. radial groove
    b. medial epicondyle
    c. lateral epicondyle
    d. deltoid tuberosity
    e. coronoid process

    Answer: d

40. The radius articulates with the
    a. humerus
    b. ulna
    c. scapula
    d. metacarpals
    e. all of the above

    Answer: b

41. The _____ of the radius assists in the stabilization of the wrist joint.
    a. olecranon process
    b. coronoid process
    c. styloid process
    d. radial tuberosity
    e. capitulum

    Answer: c

42. The bones that form the wrist are the
    a. carpals
    b. tarsals
    c. metacarpals
    d. metatarsals
    e. phalanges

    Answer: a

43. The bones that form the palms of the hands are the
    a. carpals
    b. tarsals
    c. metacarpals
    d. metatarsals
    e. phalanges

    Answer: c

44. The bones that form the fingers are the
    a. carpals
    b. tarsals
    c. metacarpals
    d. metatarsals
    e. phalanges

    Answer: e

45. The longest and heaviest bone in the body is the
    a. humerus
    b. femur
    c. tibia
    d. fibula
    e. coxa

    Answer: b

46. The distal end of the tibia articulates with the
    a. talus
    b. fibula
    c. patella
    d. calcaneus
    e. coxa

    Answer: a

47. The medial knob at the ankle is a projection from the
    a. fibula
    b. femur
    c. tibia
    d. calcaneus
    e. talus

    Answer: c

48. The fibula articulates with the
    a. femur
    b. tibia
    c. patella
    d. navicular
    e. all of the above

    Answer: b

49. The ankle contains _____ bones.
    a. 2
    b. 5
    c. 6
    d. 7
    e. 8

    Answer: d

50. Which of the following is the heel bone?
    a. talus
    b. navicular
    c. calcaneus
    d. cuboid
    e. none of the above

Answer: c

51. The sole of the foot is supported by the
    a. metacarpals
    b. metatarsals
    c. carpals
    d. tarsals
    e. both b and d

Answer: e

52. The portion of the sternum that articulates with the clavicles is the
    a. manubrium
    b. body
    c. xiphoid process
    d. angle
    e. tuberculum

Answer: a

53. The foramen magnum would be found in the
    a. frontal bone
    b. parietal bone
    c. sphenoid bone
    d. occipital bone
    e. temporal bone

Answer: d

54. The suture which forms the articulation of the two parietal bones is the
    a. lamboidal suture
    b. rostral suture
    c. coronal suture
    d. squamosal suture
    e. sagittal suture

Answer: e

55. The zygomatic arch is formed by the union of processes from which two bones?
    a. temporal bone and maxilla
    b. frontal bone and temporal bone
    c. sphenoid bone and temporal bone
    d. zygomatic bone and maxilla
    e. temporal bone and zygomatic bone

    Answer: e

56. The external auditory meatus would be found in the
    a. sphenoid bone
    b. zygomatic bone
    c. temporal bone
    d. parietal bone
    e. occipital bone

    Answer: c

57. The prominent bulge just posterior and inferior to the external auditory meatus is the
    a. mastoid process
    b. styloid process
    c. occipital condyle
    d. condyloid process
    e. temporal process

    Answer: a

58. The bony portion of the nasal septum is formed by the
    a. nasal bones
    b. perpendicular plate of the ethmoid bone
    c. perpendicular plate of the ethmoid bone and vomer
    d. vomer and sphenoid bone
    e. perpendicular plate of the ethmoid bone and sphenoid bone

    Answer: c

59. Ligaments that support the hyoid bone are attached to the
    a. styloid process
    b. mastoid process
    c. articular tubercle
    d. greater tubercle
    e. middle conchae

    Answer: a

60. The lower jaw articulates with the temporal bone at the
    a. mandibular fossa
    b. mastoid process
    c. greater tubercle
    d. foramen rotumdum
    e. cribriform plate

    Answer: a

61. The sella turcica contains the
    a. lacrimal gland
    b. pituitary gland
    c. olfactory organs
    d. nasal gland
    e. salivary gland

    Answer: b

62. The bony roof of the mouth is formed by the
    a. palatine bones
    b. vomer
    c. maxillae
    d. sphenoid bone
    e. both a and c

    Answer: e

63. The hyoid bone
    a. serves as a base of attachment for muscles that move the tongue
    b. is part of the mandible
    c. is located inferior to the larynx
    d. b and c only
    e. all of the above

    Answer: a

64. The paranasal sinuses are located in the _____ bone.
    a. frontal
    b. ethmoid
    c. sphenoid
    d. maxillae
    e. all of the above

    Answer: e

65. One role of the fontanels is to
    a. allow for compression of the skull during childbirth
    b. serve as ossification centers for the facial bones
    c. serve as the final bony plates of the skull
    d. lighten the weight of the skull bones
    e. none of the above

    Answer: a

66. The four curves of the adult spinal column are not all present at birth. Which of the following are the secondary curves, or those that do not appear until several months later?
    a. cervical and lumbar
    b. thoracic and lumbar
    c. sacral and lumbar
    d. thoracic and sacral
    e. cervical and sacral

    Answer: a

67. An exaggerated lateral curvature is termed
    a. kyphosis
    b. lordosis
    c. scoliosis
    d. gomphosis
    e. none of the above

    Answer: c

68. The vertebral column contains _____ cervical vertebrae.
    a. 4
    b. 5
    c. 7
    d. 12
    e. 31

    Answer: c

69. Cervical vertebrae can usually be distinguished from other vertebrae by the presence of
    a. transverse processes
    b. transverse foramina
    c. facets for articulation of ribs
    d. large spinous processes
    e. none of the above

    Answer: b

70. The odontoid process would be found on the
    a. atlas
    b. axis
    c. sacrum
    d. coccyx
    e. ribs

Answer: b

71. Costal processes are located on _____ vertebrae.
    a. cervical
    b. thoracic
    c. lumbar
    d. sacral
    e. coccygeal

Answer: b

72. The vertebral column contains _____ thoracic vertebrae.
    a. 4
    b. 5
    c. 7
    d. 12
    e. 31

Answer: d

73. Thoracic vertebrae can be distinguished from other vertebrae by the presence of
    a. transverse processes
    b. transverse foramina
    c. facets for the articulation of ribs
    d. notched spinous processes
    e. costal cartilages

Answer: c

74. The vertebral column contains _____ lumbar vertebrae.
    a. 4
    b. 5
    c. 7
    d. 12
    e. 31

Answer: b

75. The side walls of the vertebral foramina are formed by the
    a. spinous process
    b. body of the vertebrae
    c. pedicles
    d. laminae
    e. transverse processes

    Answer: c

76. The ribs articulate with the
    a. spinous process of the vertebra
    b. transverse process of the vertebra
    c. lamina of the vertebra
    d. pedicles of the vertebra
    e. a and b

    Answer: b

77. Humans have _____ pairs of ribs.
    a. 2
    b. 6
    c. 10
    d. 12
    e. 24

    Answer: d

78. The sacrum is composed of _____ fused vertebrae.
    a. 2
    b. 3
    c. 4
    d. 5
    e. 6

    Answer: d

79. The coccyx is composed of _____ fused vertebrae.
    a. 1-2
    b. 3-5
    c. 6-7
    d. 7-8
    e. 9-11

    Answer: b

80. Structural characteristics of the pectoral girdle that adapt it to a wide range of movement include
    a. heavy bones
    b. relatively weak joints
    c. limited range of motion at the shoulder joint
    d. joints stabilized by ligaments and tendons
    e. all of the above

    Answer: b

81. The pectoral girdle contains the
    a. humerus
    b. manubrium
    c. sternum
    d. scapula
    e. all of the above

    Answer: d

82. What tissue is primarily responsible for stabilizing, positioning, and bracing the pectoral girdle?
    a. tendons
    b. ligaments
    c. joints
    d. muscles
    e. none of the above

    Answer: d

83. Which end of the clavicle is the larger end?
    a. sternal
    b. acromial
    c. dorsal
    d. superior
    e. inferior

    Answer: b

84. The bone that articulates with the scapula at the glenoid fossa is the
    a. radius
    b. ulna
    c. humerus
    d. femur
    e. tibia

    Answer: c

85. The clavicle articulates with the scapula at the
    a. acromion process
    b. coracoid process
    c. glenoid tuberosity
    d. scapular spine
    e. subscapular fossa

    Answer: a

86. Structural characteristics of the pelvic girdle that adapt it to the role of bearing the weight of the body include
    a. heavy bones
    b. strong and stable joints
    c. a high degree of flexibility at the hip joint
    d. a and b only
    e. all of the above

    Answer: d

87. Each of the following bones is part of the pelvic girdle **except** one. Identify the exception.
    a. ilium
    b. ischium
    c. pubis
    d. coxa
    e. femur

    Answer: e

88. Which of the following is **not** a part of the pelvis?
    a. sacrum
    b. coccyx
    c. coxae
    d. lumbar vertebrae
    e. both b and d

    Answer: d

89. What bone articulates with the coxa at the acetabulum?
    a. sacrum
    b. femur
    c. humerus
    d. tibia
    e. fibula

    Answer: b

90. Each coxa is formed by the fusion of _____ bones.
    a. 2
    b. 3
    c. 4
    d. 5
    e. 6

    Answer: b

91. The largest coxal bone is the
    a. pubis
    b. ischium
    c. ilium
    d. femur
    e. tibia

    Answer: c

92. The superior border of the ilium that acts as a point of attachment for both ligaments and muscles is the
    a. anterior iliac spine
    b. acetabulum
    c. posterior superior iliac spine
    d. iliac crest
    e. iliac notch

    Answer: d

93. An immovable joint is a(n)
    a. synarthrosis
    b. diarthrosis
    c. amphiarthrosis
    d. syndesmosis
    e. symphysis

    Answer: a

94. A slightly movable joint is a(n)
    a. synarthrosis
    b. diarthrosis
    c. amphiarthrosis
    d. gomphosis
    e. synostosis

    Answer: c

95. A freely movable joint is a(n)
    a. synarthrosis
    b. diarthrosis
    c. amphiarthrosis
    d. syndesmosis
    e. symphysis

    Answer: b

96. A suture would be an example of a(n)
    a. synarthrosis
    b. syndesmosis
    c. symphysis
    d. diathrosis
    e. amphiarthrosis

    Answer: a

97. A synovial joint is an example of a(n)
    a. synarthrosis
    b. amphiarthrosis
    c. diarthrosis
    d. symphysis
    e. syndesmosis

    Answer: c

98. Which of the following is not a function of synovial fluid?
    a. shock absorption
    b. increase osmotic pressure within joint
    c. lubrication
    d. provide nutrients
    e. protect articular cartilages

    Answer: b

99. The joint that permits the greatest range of mobility of any joint in the body is the
    a. hip joint
    b. shoulder joint
    c. elbow joint
    d. knee joint
    e. wrist joint

    Answer: b

100. The elbow joint is an example of a(n)
     a. saddle joint
     b. gliding joint
     c. ellipsoid joint
     d. hinge joint
     e. pivot joint

     Answer: d

101. Decreasing the angle between bones is termed
     a. flexion
     b. extension
     c. abduction
     d. adduction
     e. hyperextension

     Answer: a

102. A movement towards the midline of the body is termed
     a. inversion
     b. abduction
     c. adduction
     d. flexion
     e. extension

     Answer: c

103. The special movement of the thumb that allows it to grasp an object and hold on to it is called
     a. rotation
     b. opposition
     c. circumduction
     d. eversion
     e. retraction

     Answer: b

104. A twisting motion of the foot that runs the sole inward is termed
     a. eversion
     b. protraction
     c. dorsiflextion
     d. plantar flexion
     e. inversion

     Answer: e

105. The opposite movement of pronation is
    a. dorsiflexion
    b. hyperextension
    c. circumduction
    d. supination
    e. rotation

    Answer: d

106. The movements known as dorsiflexion and plantar flexion involve moving the
    a. hand
    b. arm
    c. foot
    d. leg
    e. hip

    Answer: c

107. Which of the following is **not** a function of the intervertebral disc?
    a. act as shock absorbers
    b. prevent bone-to-bone contact
    c. lubricate the joint
    d. contribute to the height of the individual
    e. allow the movements associated with flexion and rotation of the vertebral column

    Answer: c

108. In the knee joint, the medial and lateral menisci
    a. are cartilages that bond the knee to the tibia
    b. act as cushions and conform to the shape of the articulating surfaces
    c. take the place of bursae
    d. are found between the patella and femur
    e. all of the above

    Answer: e

109. The knee joint is reinforced by
    a. cruciate ligaments
    b. fibular (lateral) collateral ligaments
    c. patellar ligaments
    d. tibial (medial) collateral ligaments
    e. all of the above

    Answer: e

110. The body system that is responsible for synthesizing vitamin D_3 is
    a. endocrine
    b. digestive
    c. cardiovascular
    d. urinary
    e. integumentary

Answer: a

111. How would increasing the proportion of organic molecules to inorganic components in the bony matrix affect the physical characteristics of bone?
    a. The bones would be less flexible.
    b. The bones would be stronger.
    c. The bones would be more brittle.
    d. The bones would be more flexible.
    e. The bones would be less compressible.

Answer: d

112. In compact bone, the osteons
    a. are lined up parallel to the long axis
    b. are lined up perpendicular to the long axis
    c. are arranged in an irregular pattern
    d. are separated by medullary spaces
    e. are lacking in the diaphysis

Answer: a

113. When the epiphyseal plate is replaced by bone
    a. puberty begins
    b. bones begin to grow in length
    c. appositional bone growth begins
    d. long bones have reached their adult length
    e. the bone becomes more brittle

Answer: d

114. Which is greater?
    a. osteoclast activity when calcitonin is present
    b. osteoclast activity when calcitonin is absent

Answer: b

115. Which is greater?
    a. blood calcium levels when parathyroid hormone is increased
    b. blood calcium levels when parathyroid hormone is decreased

Answer: a

116. Dislocations involving synovial joints are usually prevented by
    a. structures such as ligaments that stabilize and support the joint
    b. the shape of the articulating surface
    c. the presence of other bones that prevent certain movements
    d. the position of muscles and fat pads that limit the degree of movement
    e. all of the above

    Answer: e

117. The thickest intervertebral discs are found in the
    a. cervical region
    b. thoracic region
    c. lumbar region
    d. sacral region
    e. coccygeal region

    Answer: c

118. Damage to the temporal bone would most likely affect the sense of
    a. sight
    b. taste
    c. smell
    d. hearing
    e. touch

    Answer: d

119. As you proceed from the head inferiorly down the vertebral column,
    a. the vertebrae become larger
    b. the transverse processes become shorter
    c. the body of the vertebrae become heavier
    d. the spinous processes become larger
    e. all of the above

    Answer: e

120. Improper administration of CPR (cardiopulmonary resuscitation) can force the _____ into the liver.
    a. floating ribs
    b. lumbar vertebrae
    c. manubrium of the sternum
    d. costal cartilage
    e. xiphoid process

    Answer: e

121. The only fixed support for the pectoral girdle is the
    a. scapula
    b. clavicle
    c. humerus
    d. sternum
    e. shoulder musculature

    Answer: b

122. When standing normally, most of your weight is transmitted to the ground by the
    a. talus and calcaneus
    b. talus and cuneiforms
    c. calcaneus and cuneiforms
    d. cuboid and cuneiforms
    e. calcaneus and cuboid

    Answer: a

123. The stronger and more stable a joint is.
    a. the more mobility it has.
    b. the less mobility it has.

    Answer: b

124. Nodding your head up and down is an example of
    a. lateral and medial rotation
    b. circumduction
    c. flexion and extension
    d. pronation and supination
    e. protraction and retraction

    Answer: c

125. Which of the following movements would you associate with chewing food?
    a. elevation
    b. abduction
    c. flexion
    d. pronation
    e. circumduction

    Answer: a

126. The joints that are subjected to the greatest forces would be found in the
    a. legs
    b. arms
    c. head
    d. shoulder
    e. none of the above

    Answer: a

127. Which of the following conditions would you possible observe in a child that is suffering from vitamin D deficiency?
   a. abnormally short arms and legs
   b. abnormally long arms and legs
   c. oversized facial bones
   d. bow legs
   e. weak, brittle bones

   Answer: d

128. Mike gets into a fight and sustains a blow to the nose. Which of the following bones might be fractured by this blow?
   a. ethmoid
   b. sphenoid
   c. frontal
   d. zygomatic
   e. maxilla

   Answer: a

129. Types of tissue found in bones include all of the following **except**:
   a. blood
   b. cartilage
   c. fibrous connective tissue
   d. nerve tissue
   e. muscle tissue

   Answer: e

130. Inadequate ossification as a result of the aging process is termed:
   a. osteogenesis
   b. osteoporosis
   c. osteopenia
   d. rickets
   e. osteomalacia

   Answer: c

131. The term used to describe any bony projection or bump is:
   a. ramus
   b. fossa
   c. sulcus
   d. process
   e. meatus

   Answer: c

132. The term used to describe a shallow depression is:
    a. trochanter
    b. condyle
    c. fossa
    d. sinus
    e. ramus

    Answer: d

133. Types of synarthrotic joints include all of the following **except**:
    a. syndesmosis
    b. suture
    c. gomphosis
    d. synchondrosis
    e. all are synarthrotic joints

    Answer: a

134. Bones that develop from membranous connective tissue are called:
    a. inorganic bones
    b. organic bones
    c. ossified bones
    d. intramembranous bones
    e. endochondral bones

    Answer: d

135. The longest bone in the human body is the:
    a. radius
    b. femur
    c. ulna
    d. tibia
    e. fibula

    Answer: b

136. The largest bone in the foot is the:
    a. navicular
    b. talus
    c. calcaneus
    d. cuneiform
    e. cuboid

    Answer: c

137. The smallest bone of the wrist is the:
    a. pisiform
    b. lunate
    c. scaphoid
    d. capitate
    e. trapezoid

    Answer: a

138. The parts of the sternum include all of the following **except**:
    a. manubrium
    b. body
    c. transverse foramina
    d. xiphoid process
    e. A and C

    Answer: c

Fill-In-The-Blank

139. _____ is a general term that indicates pain and stiffness affecting the skeletal or muscular systems or both.

    Answer: Rheumatism

140. The presence of a(n) _____ _____ indicates that the long bone is still growing.

    Answer: epiphyseal disk/plate

141. Cells that are found in the exposed matrix area of the endosteum that dissolve the bony matrix are the _____.

    Answer: osteoclasts

142. The shaft of long bones is called the _____.

    Answer: diaphysis

143. The head of a long bone is called the _____.

    Answer: epiphysis

144. _____ _____ prevents direct bone-to-bone contact within movable joints.

    Answer: Articular cartilage

145. During the process of _____, an existing tissue is replaced by bone.

    Answer: ossicifation

146. The process of depositing calcium into a tissue is called _____.

    Answer: calcification

147. Damage to a bone because of extreme load, sudden impact, or stresses applied from an unusual direction is called a(n) _____.

    Answer: fracture

148. An increase in the diameter of growing bone is termed _____ _____.

    Answer: appositional growth or diametric growth

149. Two hormones that work together to elevate calcium levels in the body are _____ _____ and _____.

    Answer: parathyroid hormone and calcitriol

150. Any projection or bump on a bone is termed a _____.

    Answer: process

151. The expanded articular end of an epiphysis that is separated from the shaft by a narrower neck is termed a _____.

    Answer: head

152. A smooth, grooved articular process shaped like a pulley is termed a _____.

    Answer: trochlea

153. A _____ is an opening for blood vessels and/or nerves.

    Answer: foramen

154. True ribs are directly connected to the sternum by _____ _____.

    Answer: costal cartilage

155. Ribs that have no direct connection to the sternum are called _____ _____.

Answer: floating ribs

156. Ribs 8 through 10 are called _____ ribs because they do not attach directly to the sternum.

Answer: false

157. The bony compartment that houses the brain is called the _____.

Answer: cranium

158. The occipital bone articulates with the first cervical vertebra at the _____ _____.

Answer: occipital condyles

159. The parietal bones interlock along the _____ suture.

Answer: sagittal

160. The frontal and parietal bones articulate at the _____ suture.

Answer: coronal

161. The fibrous areas that exist between cranial bones at birth are called _____.

Answer: fontanels

162. Successive vertebrae articulate at gliding joints between _____ and _____ articular processes.

Answer: superior and inferior

163. The first cervical vertebra is also known as the _____.

Answer: atlas

164. The second cervical vertebra is also known as the _____.

Answer: axis

165. The appendicular skeleton includes the bones of the upper and lower extremities and the supporting elements called _____.

Answer: girdles

166. Posteriorly, the ilium articulates with the sacrum at the _____ joint.

   Answer: sacroiliac

167. The location where two bones meet is called a(n) _____.

   Answer: articulation (joint)

168. _____ subdivide synovial cavities, channel the flow of synovial fluid, and allow for variations in the shapes of the articular surfaces.

   Answer: Menisci

169. Pads of _____ are often found around the edges of joints to provide protection for the articular cartilages.

   Answer: fat or adipose

170. Small pockets of synovial fluid that form to reduce friction and act as a shock absorber where ligaments and tendons rub against other tissues are called _____.

   Answer: bursae

171. Extending a body part past the anatomical position is called _____.

   Answer: hyperextension

172. The movement of rotating a limb toward the ventral surface of the body is called medial _____.

   Answer: medial rotation

173. The movement of rotating a limb outward is called _____ _____.

   Answer: lateral rotation

174. The movement of a body part forward in a horizontal plane is called _____

   Answer: protraction

175. The movement of a body part backward in a horizontal plane is called _____.

   Answer: retraction

176. The movement of a body part superiorly is called _____.

    Answer: elevation

177. The movement of a body part inferiorly is called _____.

    Answer: depression

Matching

178. Match the term in the first column with the definition in the second column.

    _____1. condyle   A. prominent ridge
    _____2. crest   B. smooth, grooved articular process
    _____3. antrum   C. expanded end of an epiphysis
    _____4. trochlea   D. chamber within a bone
    _____5. head   E. smooth, rounded articular process

    Answer: 1-e, 2-a, 3-d, 4-b, 5-c

179. Match the bone in the first column with the feature in the second column

    _____1. femur   A. linea aspera
    _____2. tibia   B. lateral malleolus
    _____3. fibula   C. medial malleolus

    Answer: 1-a, 2-c, 3-b

Essay

180. Differentiate between compact bone and spongy bone.

    Answer:
    Compact bone has osteons situated in closely packed areas and is found where stresses come from a limited range of directions. Spongy bone has large spaces between thin, bony plates and is found where stresses are few or come from many different directions. Compact bone provides strength; whereas, spongy bone serves to reduce the weight of bones.

181. Mary is in her last month of pregnancy and is suffering from lower back pains. Since she is carrying her excess weight in front of her, she wonders why her back hurts. What would you tell her?

    Answer:
    Women in later stages of pregnancy develop lower back pain because of changes in the lumbar curvature of the spine. The increased mass of the pregnant uterus shifts the center of gravity; to compensate for this, the lumbar curvature is exaggerated and more of the body weight is supported by the lumbar region than normal. This results in sore muscles and the lower back pain.

182. Billy is injured during a high school football game. His chest is badly bruised and he is experiencing difficulty breathing. What might be the problem?

    Answer:
    Billy has probably broken one or more of his ribs. Movement of the ribs change the size of the thoracic cavity, which is an important part of breathing. When the ribs are broken, breathing can become difficult (labored) because the ribs cannot function properly. It is also possible that the injury caused a rib to pierce one of the lungs, resulting in a condition known as a pneumothorax, or collapsed lung due to air in the pleural cavity.

183. Due to a developmental defect, Mike was born without clavicles. As a result of this condition, what would you expect in terms of upper body motion?

    Answer: Mike would have an increased range of motion at the shoulder joint.

184. Why would a person suffering from osteoporosis be more likely to suffer a broken hip than a broken shoulder?

    Answer:
    In osteoporosis, a decrease in the calcium content of bones leads to bones that are weak and brittle. Since the hip joint and leg bones must support the weight of the body, any weakening of these bones may result in not enough strength to support the body mass, and as a result the bone will break under the great weight. The shoulder joint is not a load-bearing joint and is not subject to the same great stresses or strong muscle contractions as the hip joint. As a result, fractures in the bones of this joint should occur less frequently.

185. When playing a contact sport, which injury would you expect to occur more frequently, a dislocated shoulder or a dislocated hip? Why?

    Answer:
    Shoulder dislocations would occur more frequently than hip dislocations because the shoulder is a more mobile joint. Because of its mobility, the shoulder joint is not bound tightly by ligaments or other structures and is easier to dislocate when excessive forces are applied. The hip joint, although mobile, is stabilized by four heavy ligaments and bones fit together snugly in the joint. The synovial capsule of the hip joint is larger than the shoulder and the range of motion is not as great. These factors contribute to the joint being more stable and less easily dislocated.

Chapter 7: The Muscular System

Multiple Choice

1. Which of the following is a function of skeletal muscle?
   a. produce movement
   b. maintain posture
   c. maintain body temperature
   d. a and b only
   e. all of the above

   Answer: e

2. Which of the following statements is **incorrect**?
   a. the contractions of skeletal muscles pull on tendons and move elements of the skeleton
   b. skeletal muscles are responsible for guarding the openings of the digestive and urinary tracts
   c. skeletal muscles are responsible for the pumping action of the heart
   d. skeletal muscles support the weight of some internal organs
   e. skeletal muscle contractions help maintain body temperature

   Answer: c

3. The dense layer of collagen fibers that surround an entire skeletal muscle is the
   a. tendon
   b. epimysium
   c. endomysium
   d. perimysium
   e. fascicle

   Answer: b

4. Nerves and blood vessels that service the muscle fibers are located in the connective tissues of the
   a. endomysium
   b. perimysium
   c. sarcolemma
   d. sarcomere
   e. myofibrils

   Answer: b

5. The delicate connective tissue that surrounds the skeletal muscle fibers and ties adjacent muscle fibers together is the
   a. endomysium
   b. perimysium
   c. epimysium
   d. sarcolemma
   e. periosteum

   Answer: a

6. The bundle of collagen fibers at the end of a skeletal muscle that attaches the muscle to bone is called a(n)
    a. fascicle
    b. tendon
    c. ligament
    d. epimysium
    e. myofibril

Answer: b

7. Skeletal muscle fibers differ from "typical cells" in that these muscle fibers
    a. lack a cell membrane
    b. have many nuclei
    c. are very small
    d. lack mitochondria
    e. all of the above

Answer: b

8. The advantage of having many nuclei in a skeletal muscle fiber is
    a. the ability to contract
    b. the ability to produce more ATP with little oxygen
    c. the ability to repair the fiber after an injury
    d. the ability to produce large amounts of the enzymes and structural proteins needed for contraction
    e. all of the above

Answer: d

9. The cell membrane of skeletal muscle is called the
    a. sarcolemma
    b. sarcomere
    c. sarcosome
    d. sarcoplasmic reticulum
    e. sarcoplasm

Answer: a

10. The cytoplasm of a skeletal muscle fiber is called the
    a. sarcolemma
    b. sarcomere
    c. sarcosome
    d. sarcoplasmic reticulum
    e. sarcoplasm

Answer: e

11. The command to contract is distributed throughout a muscle fiber by the
    a. sarcolemma
    b. sarcomere
    c. transverse tubules
    d. myotubules
    e. myofibrils

    Answer: c

12. The membranous network of channels within a muscle fiber is the
    a. sarcolemma
    b. sarcoplasmic reticulum
    c. myolemma
    d. sarcoplasm
    e. none of the above

    Answer: b

13. The functional unit of skeletal muscle is the
    a. sarcolemma
    b. sarcomere
    c. sarcoplasmic reticulum
    d. myofibril
    e. myofilament

    Answer: b

14. Interactions between actin and myosin filaments of the sarcomere are responsible for
    a. muscle fatigue
    b. the conduction of neural information to the muscle fiber
    c. muscle contraction
    d. muscle relaxation
    e. the striped appearance of skeletal muscle

    Answer: c

15. Thin filaments at either end of the sarcomere are attached to the
    a. Z line
    b. M line
    c. H band
    d. A band
    e. I band

    Answer: a

16. The area of the sarcomere containing the thick filaments is the
    a. Z line
    b. M line
    c. H band
    d. A band
    e. I band

    Answer: d

17. The area of the sarcomere that contains only thin filaments is the
    a. Z line
    b. M line
    c. H band
    d. A band
    e. I band

    Answer: e

18. Each thin filament consists of
    a. a pair of protein strands wound together
    b. chains of myosin molecules
    c. 6 molecules coiled into a helical structure
    d. a rod-shaped structure with "heads" projecting from each end
    e. a double strand of myosin molecules

    Answer: a

19. The sarcoplasmic reticulum stores
    a. oxygen
    b. glycogen
    c. ATP
    d. calcium ions
    e. glucose

    Answer: d

20. The complex known as the triad consists of
    a. actin, myosin, and myofilaments
    b. transverse tubule and terminal cistemae
    c. myofilaments, myofibrils, and sarcomeres
    d. A bands, H bands, and I bands
    e. actin, myosin, and sarcomeres

    Answer: b

21. Cross-bridges are located on
    a. actin molecules
    b. myosin molecules
    c. troponin molecules
    d. tropomyosin molecules
    e. calcium ions

Answer: b

22. At rest, active sites on the actin are blocked by
    a. myosin molecules
    b. troponin molecules
    c. tropomyosin molecules
    d. ATP molecules
    e. calcium ions

Answer: c

23. At rest, the tropomyosin molecule is held in place by
    a. actin molecules
    b. myosin molecules
    c. troponin molecules
    d. ATP molecules
    e. calcium ions

Answer: c

24. The point of near-contact between a skeletal muscle fiber and its controlling motor neuron is the
    a. synaptic knob
    b. motor end plate
    c. neuromuscular junction
    d. synaptic cleft
    e. transverse tubule

Answer: c

25. The _____ contains vesicles filled with acetylcholine.
    a. synaptic knob
    b. motor end plate
    c. neuromuscular junction
    d. synaptic cleft
    e. transverse tubule

Answer: a

26. The space between the neuron and the muscle is the
    a. synaptic knob
    b. motor end plate
    c. motor unit
    d. synaptic cleft
    e. I band

    Answer: d

27. Active sites on actin become available for binding when
    a. actin binds to troponin
    b. troponin binds to tropomyosin
    c. calcium binds to troponin
    d. calcium binds to tropomyosin
    e. myosin binds to troponin

    Answer: c

28. In response to action potentials arriving from the transverse tubules, the sarcoplasmic reticulum releases
    a. acetylcholine
    b. sodium ions
    c. potassium ions
    d. calcium ions
    e. all of the above

    Answer: d

29. When a calcium ion binds to troponin,
    a. tropomyosin moves out of the groove between the actin molecules
    b. active sites on the myosin are exposed
    c. actin heads will bind to myosin
    d. muscle relaxation occurs
    e. all of the above

    Answer: a

30. The type of contraction represented by a single stimulus-contraction-relaxation sequence is
    a. a twitch
    b. tetany
    c. recovery
    d. recruitment
    e. a spasm

    Answer: a

31. Calcium ions are released from the sarcoplasmic reticulum during the
_____ phase of contraction.
    a. latent
    b. contraction
    c. twitch
    d. relaxation
    e. recovery

Answer: a

32. The smooth but steady increase in muscle tension produced by increasing
the number of active motor units is called
    a. tetany
    b. a twitch
    c. relaxation
    d. recovery
    e. recruitment

Answer: e

33. The type of contraction in which the muscle fibers produce increased
tension, but do not shorten is called
    a. tetany
    b. a twitch
    c. recruitment
    d. isotonic
    e. isometric

Answer: e

34. A resting muscle generates most of its ATP by
    a. conversion of creatine phosphate
    b. anaerobic respiration
    c. aerobic respiration
    d. the tricarboxylic acid cycle
    e. c and d

Answer: c

35. Creatine phosphate
    a. is produced by the process of anaerobic respiration
    b. can replace ATP in binding to myosin molecules during contraction
    c. acts as an energy reserve in muscle tissue
    d. is only formed during strenuous exercise
    e. cannot transfer its phosphate group to ADP

Answer: c

36. During anaerobic respiration that is termed glycolysis
    a. ATP is produced
    b. pyruvic acid is produced
    c. NAD is oxidized
    d. a and b only
    e. all of the above

    Answer: d

37. When energy reserves in a muscle are exhausted or lactic acid levels increase
    a. an oxygen debt is repaid
    b. fatigue occurs
    c. relaxation occurs
    d. tetany occurs
    e. atrophy occurs

    Answer: b

38. Fast fibers
    a. have high resistance to fatigue
    b. have a high concentration of myoglobin
    c. have many mitochondria
    d. contract quickly
    e. all of the above

    Answer: d

39. The type of muscle fiber that is best adapted for endurance is the
    a. fast fiber
    b. slow fiber
    c. intermediate fiber
    d. anaerobic fiber
    e. high density fiber

    Answer: b

40. Activities that require anaerobic endurance
    a. require maximal contraction of muscles for short periods of time
    b. do not use ATP very quickly
    c. usually do not cause an individual to develop an oxygen debt
    d. do not rely on the energy reserves of creatine phosphate
    e. all of the above

    Answer: a

41. During activities requiring aerobic endurance
    a. glycogen and glycolysis are the primary sources of reserve energy
    b. oxygen debts are common
    c. most of the muscle's energy is produced in mitochondria
    d. fatigue occurs in a few minutes
    e. all of the above

    Answer: c

42. Which of the following is **not** characteristic of smooth muscle?
    a. Smooth muscle fibers are uninucleate.
    b. Neurons that innervate smooth muscles are under voluntary control.
    c. Smooth muscles are not striated.
    d. Smooth muscles do not contain sarcomeres.
    e. Smooth muscles may be tetanized.

    Answer: b

43. Which of the following is **not** characteristic of cardiac muscle?
    a. Cardiac muscles are not striated.
    b. Cardiac muscles cannot be tetanized.
    c. Cardiac muscle fibers are uninucleate.
    d. Cardiac muscles contain sarcomeres.
    e. Neurons that innervate cardiac muscles are under involuntary control.

    Answer: a

44. The more moveable end of a muscle is the
    a. insertion
    b. belly
    c. origin
    d. proximal end
    e. distal end

    Answer: a

45. A muscle that inserts on the body of the mandible is probably involved in
    a. kissing
    b. blowing
    c. chewing
    d. frowning
    e. wrinkling the forehead

    Answer: c

46. A muscle that inserts on the greater tubercle of the humerus is most likely involved in
    a. flexion
    b. extension
    c. lateral rotation
    d. medial rotation
    e. abduction

    Answer: c

47. Muscles that insert on the olecranon process of the ulna probably act to
    a. flex the forearm
    b. extend the forearm
    c. abduct the forearm
    d. adduct the forearm
    e. none of the above

    Answer: b

48. A muscle that assists the muscle that is primarily responsible for a given action is a(n)
    a. agonist
    b. antagonist
    c. synergist
    d. originator
    e. levator

    Answer: c

49. Each of the following terms is a descriptive word for a muscle's action **except** one. Identify the exception.
    a. levator
    b. extensor
    c. tensor
    d. buccinator
    e. adductor

    Answer: d

50. Muscles ending in the suffix -costal would be found in the
    a. head
    b. neck
    c. chest
    d. abdomen
    e. groin

    Answer: c

51. Which of the following is **not** a muscle of facial expression?
    a. buccinator
    b. zygomaticus
    c. orbicularis oculi
    d. masseter
    e. depressor anguli oris

    Answer: d

52. The "kissing muscle" that purses the lips is the
    a. zygomaticus
    b. orbicularis oris
    c. buccinator
    d. orbicularis oculi
    e. temporalis

    Answer: b

53. The origin of the frontalis muscle is the
    a. mandible
    b. frontal bone
    c. occipital bone
    d. galea aponeurotica
    e. temporal bone

    Answer: d

54. Which of the following describes the action of the digastricus?
    a. elevates the larynx
    b. elevates the larynx and depresses the mandible
    c. depresses the larynx
    d. depresses and retracts the tongue
    e. elevates the mandible

    Answer: b

55. The muscle which inserts on the coronoid process of the mandible is the
    a. temporalis
    b. masseter
    c. lateral pterygoid
    d. medial pterygoid
    e. platysma

    Answer: a

56. Which of the following is a spinal flexor?
    a. iliocostalis
    b. spinalis
    c. longissimus
    d. quadratus lumborum
    e. both a and b

    Answer: d

57. The iliac crest is the origin of the
    a. qadratus lumborum
    b. iliocostalis
    c. longissimus
    d. semispinalis
    e. both b and d

    Answer: a

58. Which of the following muscles has its insertion on the cartilages of the ribs?
    a. internal oblique
    b. external intercostals
    c. transversus abdominis
    d. internal intercostals
    e. both a and b

    Answer: a

59. The muscle which inserts on the superior surface of the pubis around the symphysis is the
    a. internal oblique
    b. external oblique
    c. rectus abdominis
    d. transversus abdominis
    e. diaphragm

    Answer: c

60. Which of the following muscles compresses the abdomen?
    a. diaphragm
    b. serratus anterior
    c. rectus abdominis
    d. transversus abdominis
    e. both a and d

    Answer: d

61. The spinal processes of the upper thoracic vertebrae are the origin of the
    a. levator scapulae
    b. rhomboideus major
    c. subclacvius
    d. supraspinatus
    e. pectoralis major

    Answer: b

62. Which of the following is the insertion of the pectoralis minor?
    a. the vertebral border near the spine
    b. coracoid process of the scapula
    c. mastoid region of the skull
    d. the occipital bone of the skull
    e. clavicle and scapula

    Answer: b

63. Which of the following describes the action of the serratus anterior?
    a. adducts the arm
    b. adducts and flexes the humerus
    c. protracts shoulder, abducts and medially rotates the scapula
    d. medial rotation of the humerus
    e. lateral rotation of the humerus

    Answer: c

64. Which of the following does not move the shoulder girdle?
    a. pectoralis major
    b. deltoid
    c. serratus anterior
    d. rhomboideus
    e. trapezius

    Answer: b

65. The muscle which adducts and rotates the scapula laterally is the
    a. rhomboideus
    b. levator scapulae
    c. serratus anterior
    d. pectoralis minor
    e. subclavius

    Answer: a

66. The muscle which inserts on the acromion process of the clavicle and the scapular spine is the
    a. serratus anterior
    b. trapezius
    c. sternocleidomastoid
    d. pectoralis minor
    e. levator scapulae

    Answer: b

67. All of the following originate on the scapula **except** the
    a. pectoralis major
    b. teres major
    c. teres minor
    d. subscapularis
    e. supraspinatus

    Answer: a

68. The major abductor of the upper arm is the
    a. supraspinatus
    b. subscapularis
    c. deltoid
    d. biceps brachii
    e. teres major

    Answer: c

69. The muscle which adducts and flexes the humerus is the
    a. coracobrachialis
    b. deltoid
    c. trapezius
    d. latissimus dorsi
    e. triceps brachii

    Answer: a

70. The muscle which extends the arm while doing push-ups is the
    a. deltoid
    b. pectoralis major
    c. brachialis
    d. triceps brachii
    e. biceps brachii

    Answer: d

71. Which of the following is the origin of the supinator?
    a. olecranon process of the ulna
    b. infraglenoid tuberosity of the scapula
    c. lateral epicondyle of the humerus
    d. medial epicondyle of the humerus
    e. base of the second metacarpal

    Answer: c

72. Pronation of the forearm is due to the
    a. brachialis
    b. triceps brachii
    c. pronator quadratus
    d. biceps brachii
    e. latissimus dorsi

    Answer: c

73. The muscle which inserts on the iliotibial tract and gluteal tuberosity
    of the femur is the
    a. gracilis
    b. sortorius
    c. rectus femoris
    d. gluteus medius
    e. gluteus maximus

    Answer: e

74. The muscle which originates along the entire length of the linea aspera
    of the femur is the
    a. vastus lateralis
    b. vastus medialis
    c. illiacus
    d. rectus femoris
    e. biceps femoris

    Answer: b

75. The muscle which opposes the gastrocnemius is the
    a. peroneus
    b. extensor digitorum
    c. soleus
    d. tibialis posterior
    e. tibialis anterior

    Answer: e

76. The muscle which dorsiflexes the foot is the
    a. tibialis anterior
    b. tibialis posterior
    c. soleus
    d. peroneus
    e. gastrocnemius

    Answer: a

77. The degree of relative movement is greater in the
    a. pelvic girdle
    b. pectoral girdle

    Answer: b

78. Fast muscle fibers can develop a larger number of mitochondria in response to
    a. repeated, exhaustive stimulation
    b. sustained low levels of muscle activity
    c. high amounts of oxygen
    d. increased levels of testosterone
    e. exercises like jogging and distance swimming

    Answer: a

79. In addition to the number and type of muscle fibers in a muscle, peak athletic performance requires
    a. a good blood supply and system of blood delivery
    b. a well-developed respiratory system
    c. the coordination of the nervous system
    d. good supplies of nutrients
    e. all of the above

    Answer: e

80. Each of the following changes in the skeletal muscles is a consequence of aging **except** one. Identify the exception.
    a. muscle fibers become smaller in diameter
    b. muscles become less elastic
    c. muscles fatigue more rapidly
    d. muscle fibers increase their reserves of glycogen
    e. muscle fibers become less efficient

    Answer: d

81. An increase in the amount of connective tissue in muscles is termed
    a. fibrosis
    b. atrophy
    c. hypertrophy
    d. hyperdystrophy
    e. fibromyalgia syndrome

    Answer: a

82. Which of the following hormones regulate(s) calcium and phosphate ion concentrations?
    a. growth hormone
    b. calcitonin
    c. thyroid hormone
    d. parathyroid hormone
    e. both b and d

    Answer: e

83. Vitamin D for Ca++ absorption from the intestine is synthesized by which of the following systems?
    a. lymphatic
    b. respiratory
    c. urinary
    d. integumentary
    e. skeletal

    Answer: d

84. During relaxation, muscles return to their original length because of
    a. elastic forces
    b. the contraction of opposing muscles
    c. the pull of gravity
    d. the elastic nature of the sarcolemma
    e. all of the above

    Answer: e

85. Which of the following hormones stimulates growth of muscle tissue and increased muscle mass?
    a. epinephrine
    b. thyroid hormone
    c. testosterone
    d. parathyroid hormone
    e. calcitonin

    Answer: c

86. Because skeletal muscle contractions demand large quantities of ATP, skeletal muscles have
    a. a rich nerve supply
    b. a rich vascular supply
    c. very few mitochondria
    d. little need for oxygen
    e. all of the above

    Answer: b

87. How would blocking the activity of acetylcholinesterase affect skeletal muscle?
    a. It would make the muscles less excitable.
    b. It would produce muscle weakness.
    c. It would cause spastic paralysis (muscles are contracted and unable to relax).
    d. It would cause flaccid paralysis (muscles are relaxed and unable to contract).
    e. It would have no affect on skeletal muscles.

    Answer: c

88. In which of the following would the ratio of motor neurons to muscle fibers be the greatest?
    a. large muscles of the upper arms
    b. postural muscles of the back
    c. muscles that control the eye
    d. leg muscles
    e. the calf muscle

    Answer: c

89. Which of the following muscles would contract most forcefully?
    a. a muscle receiving 10 action potentials per second
    b. a muscle receiving 20 action potentials per second

    Answer: a

90. Which of the following muscles would produce the most tension?
    a. a muscle with 20 motor units active
    b. a muscle with 10 motor units active

    Answer: a

91. Which of the following activities would employ isometric contractions?
    a. flexing the forearm
    b. chewing food
    c. maintaining an upright posture
    d. running
    e. writing

    Answer: c

92. Increased oxygen consumption would accompany
    a. increased heat production
    b. increased conversion of lactic acid to glucose
    c. increased aerobic respiration by muscle cells
    d. increased muscle activity
    e. all of the above

    Answer: e

93. A person whose genetic makeup makes them a better marathon runner than a sprinter probably has more _____ in their leg muscles.
    a. fast fibers
    b. intermediate fibers
    c. slow fibers
    d. dark fibers
    e. noncontractile fibers

    Answer: c

94. Which of the following is greater?
    a. the concentration of calcium ion in the sarcoplasm of a resting muscle
    b. the concentration of calcium ion in the sarcoplasmic reticulum of a resting muscle

    Answer: b

95. Tom is having difficulty plantar flexing and inverting his right foot. Which muscle(s) is/are most likely involved in this problem?
    a. tibialis anterior
    b. soleus
    c. gastrocnemius
    d. flexor digitorum
    e. both b and c

    Answer: e

96. The bacterium that causes tetanus produces a toxin that affects the central nervous system and skeletal muscles producing powerful tetanic contractions of the skeletal muscles. The toxin probably acts by
    a. increasing the amount of acetylcholinesterase in the synapse
    b. making the cells less permeable to sodium ions
    c. increasing the amount of potassium ion in the intercellular fluid
    d. making the cell membranes more permeable to calcium ion
    e. competing with acetylcholine for receptors on the muscle fiber membrane

    Answer: d

97. Tom, a trumpet player, asks you which muscles he should develop in order to be a better trumpeter. What would you tell him?
    a. the masseter and buccinator
    b. the buccinator and orbicularis oris
    c. the orbicularis oris and risorius
    d. the risorius and zygomaticus
    e. the levator labii and mentalis

    Answer: b

98. Muscles comprising the quadriceps group include:
    a. rectus femoris, vastus intermedialis, vastus lateralis, and vastus medialis
    b. rectus femoris, tibialis anterior, soleus, and adductor longus
    c. peroneus, gastrocnemius, vastus intermedialis, and rectus femoris
    d. iliopsoas, gracilis, adductor magnus, biceps femoris, and gracilis
    e. semitendinosis, biceps femoris, rectus femoris, and vastus medialis

    Answer: a

99. The term is used to describe a number of inherited diseases characterized by progressive muscular weakness and deterioration.
    a. multiple sclerosis
    b. muscular dystrophies
    c. polymyositis
    d. cystic fibrosis
    e. myopathies

    Answer: b

100. Rigor mortis occurs at death due to a lack of
    a. cAMP
    b. DNA
    c. RNA
    d. ATP
    e. TRNA

    Answer: d

101. The bacterium that causes tetanus is:
    a. *Clostridium botulinum*
    b. *Staphylococcus aureus*
    c. *Clostridium tetani*
    d. *Proteus vulgaris*
    e. *Pseudomonas aeruginosa*

    Answer: c

102. This condition develops when an organ protrudes through an abnormal opening.
    a. peritonitis
    b. colitis
    c. muscular dystrophy
    d. Myasthenia gravis
    e. Hernia

    Answer: e

103. Relative to the aging process, skeletal muscle fibers
    a. become larger in diameter
    b. remain the same
    c. become smaller in diameter
    d. increase in strength
    e. fatigue slowly

    Answer: c

Fill-In-The-Blank

104. The protein _____, works with myosin and is responsible for muscle contraction and relaxation.

    Answer: actin

105. A muscle _____ contains a sarcolemma, sarcoplasm, filaments, and myofibrils.

    Answer: fiber

106. A sheath of connective tissue surrounding a bundle of striated muscle fibers is called _____.

    Answer: perimysium

107. A sheath surrounding each skeletal muscle fiber is called _____.

    Answer: endomysium

Matching

108. Match the muscle in the first column with its action in the second column.

     _____1. deltoid
     _____2. pectoralis major
     _____3. biceps brachii
     _____4. triceps brachii
     _____5. flexor carpi radialis

A. flexes and abducts palm
B. abducts arm
C. extends forearm
D. flexes, adducts, and medially rotates humerus
E. flexes and supinates forearm

Answer: 1-b, 2-d, 3-e, 4-c, 5-a

Essay

109. Mary wants to enter a weight-lifting competition and consults you as to what type of muscle fibers she needs to develop and how she should go about it. What would you suggest to her?

Answer:
Weight lifting requires anaerobic endurance. Mary would want to develop her fast fibers for short-term maximum strength. She would achieve this by engaging in activities that involve frequent, brief, but intensive workouts, such as with progressive resistance machines. Repeated exhaustive stimulation will help the fast fibers develop more mitochondria and a higher concentration of glycolytic enzymes as well as increase the size and strength of the muscle (hypertrophy).

110. While unloading her car trunk, Amy pulls a muscle and as a result has difficulty moving her arm. The doctor in the emergency room tells her that she pulled her pectoralis major. Amy tells you that she thought the pectoralis major was a chest muscle and doesn't understand what that has to do with her arm. What would you tell her?

Answer:
Although the pectoralis muscle is located across the chest, it inserts on the greater tubercle of the humerus, the large bone of the upper arm. When the muscle contracts, it contributes to flexion, adduction, and medial rotation of the humerus. All of these arm movements would be in part impaired if the muscle were damaged.

Chapter 8: The Nervous System

Multiple Choice

1. Each of the following is a function of the nervous system **except** one.
   Identify the exception.
   a. providing sensation of the internal and external environments
   b. integrating sensory information
   c. coordinating voluntary and involuntary activities
   d. direct activities that continue for extended periods such as growth
      and pregnancy
   e. regulating or controlling peripheral structures and systems

   Answer: d

2. The brain and spinal cord comprise the
   a. autonomic nervous system
   b. peripheral nervous system
   c. central nervous system
   d. efferent nervous system
   e. afferent nervous system

   Answer: c

3. Voluntary control of skeletal muscles is provided by the
   a. sympathetic nervous system
   b. parasympathetic nervous system
   c. afferent nervous system
   d. somatic nervous system
   e. autonomic nervous system

   Answer: d

4. That part of the peripheral nervous system which brings information to
   the central nervous system is
   a. motor
   b. afferent
   c. efferent
   d. autonomic
   e. somatic

   Answer: b

5. Which of the following is not a function of the neuroglia?
   a. support
   b. information processing
   c. secretion of cerebrospinal fluid
   d. isolation of neurons
   e. phagocytosis

   Answer: b

6. Each of the following is a type of glial cell found in the central nervous system **except** one. Identify the exception.
   a. astrocytes
   b. Schwann cells
   c. oligodendrocytes
   d. microglia
   e. ependymal cells

Answer: b

7. The largest and most numerous of the glial cells in the central nervous system are the
   a. astrocytes
   b. Schwann cells
   c. oligodendrocytes
   d. microglia
   e. ependymal cells

Answer: a

8. The myelin sheaths that surround the axons of some of the neurons in the CNS are formed by
   a. astrocytes
   b. Schwann cells
   c. oligodendrocytes
   d. microglia
   e. ependymal cells

Answer: c

9. The type of glial cell that is found lining the ventricles and spinal canal are the
   a. astrocytes
   b. Schwann cells
   c. oligodendrocytes
   d. microglia
   e. ependymal cells

Answer: e

10. Small phagocytic cells that are especially obvious in damaged tissue in the CNS are the
   a. astrocytes
   b. Schwann cells
   c. oligodendrocytes
   d. microglia
   e. ependymal cells

Answer: d

11. The neurilemma of axons in the peripheral nervous system is formed by
    a. astrocytes
    b. ependymal cells
    c. oligodendrocytes
    d. microglia
    e. Schwann cells

    Answer: e

12. Which of the following is a glial cell of the PNS?
    a. Schwann cells
    b. astrocytes
    c. ependyma
    d. microglia
    e. oligodendrocytes

    Answer: a

13. Cells responsible for information processing and transfer are
    a. neuroglia
    b. Schwann cells
    c. neurons
    d. astrocytes
    e. microglia

    Answer: c

14. Aggregations of ribosomes in neurons are referred to as
    a. neurofilaments
    b. neurofibrils
    c. synapses
    d. Nissl bodies
    e. microglia

    Answer: d

15. The axon is connected to the soma or cell body at a region called the
    a. telodendria
    b. synaptic knobs
    c. collaterals
    d. hillock
    e. synapse

    Answer: d

16. Branches that sometimes occur along the length of an axon are called
    a. action potentials
    b. synaptic knobs
    c. collaterals
    d. hillock
    e. synapse

    Answer: c

17. Neurotransmitters are released from the
    a. dendrites
    b. synaptic knobs
    c. collaterals
    d. hillock
    e. synapse

    Answer: b

18. The site of intercellular communication between neurons is
    a. dendrite
    b. synaptic knob
    c. collateral
    d. hillock
    e. synapse

    Answer: e

19. Neurons that have one axon and one dendrite are called
    a. polypolar
    b. unipolar
    c. bipolar
    d. tripolar
    e. multipolar

    Answer: c

20. Neurons that have several dendrites and a single axon are called
    a. polypolar
    b. unipolar
    c. bipolar
    d. tripolar
    e. multipolar

    Answer: e

21. Sensory neurons of the PNS are
    a. unipolar
    b. bipolar
    c. polypolar
    d. multipolar
    e. tripolar

    Answer: a

22. Interneurons
    a. are found only in the central nervous system
    b. carry only sensory impulses
    c. carry only motor impulses
    d. only connect motor neurons to other motor neurons
    e. are found between neurons and their effectors

    Answer: a

23. Which of the following is not involved in creating the resting potential
    of a neuron?
    a. diffusion of potassium ions out of the cell
    b. diffusion of sodium ions into the cell
    c. membrane permeability for sodium ions greater than potassium ions
    d. membrane permeability for potassium ions greater than sodium ions
    e. the interior of the cell membrane has an excess of negatively charged
       protein molecules

    Answer: d

24. At the normal resting potential of a typical neuron, its ion exchange
    pumps
    a. exchange 1 intracellular sodium ion for 2 extracellular potassium
       ions
    b. exchange 2 intracellular sodium ions for 1 extracellular potassium
       ion
    c. exchange 3 intracellular sodium ions for 1 extracellular potassium
       ion
    d. exchange 3 intracellular sodium ions for 2 extracellular potassium
       ions
    e. exchange 3 extracellular sodium ions for 2 intracellular potassium
       ions

    Answer: d

25. Opening of sodium channels in the membrane of a neuron results in
    a. depolarization
    b. repolarization
    c. hyperpolarization
    d. increased negative charge inside the membrane
    e. none of the above

    Answer: a

26. The following are the main steps in the generation of an action potential.
    1. sodium channels are inactivated
    2. potassium channels open and potassium moves out of the cell initiating repolarization
    3. sodium channels regain their normal properties
    4. a graded depolarization brings an area of an excitable membrane to threshold
    5. a temporary hyperpolarization occurs
    6. sodium channel activation occurs
    7. sodium ions enter the cell and depolarization occurs

    The proper sequence of these events is
    a. 4, 6, 7, 3, 2, 5, 1
    b. 4, 6, 7, 1, 2, 3, 5
    c. 5, 7, 4, 1, 2, 3, 5
    d. 2, 4, 6, 7, 1, 3, 5
    e. 4, 2, 5, 6, 7, 3, 1

    Answer: b

27. The sodium-potassium exchange pump
    a. must re-establish ion concentrations after each action potential
    b. transports sodium ions into the cell during depolarization
    c. transports potassium ions out of the cell during repolarization
    d. moves sodium and potassium in the direction of their chemical gradients
    e. requires ATP to function

    Answer: e

28. The all-or-none principle states that
    a. all stimuli will produce identical action potentials
    b. all stimuli great enough to bring the membrane to threshold will produce identical action potentials
    c. the greater the magnitude of the stimuli, the greater the intensity of the action potential
    d. only sensory stimuli can activate action potentials
    e. only motor stimuli can activate action potentials

    Answer: b

29. During continuous conduction,
    a. action potentials move in all directions along an axon
    b. action potentials occur at successive nodes along the length of the stimulated axon
    c. local currents depolarize adjacent areas of membrane so that action potentials continue to form along the membrane
    d. action potentials produce a local current that is strong enough to spread along the length of the axon
    e. local potentials produce a continuous outward flow of potassium ions

    Answer: c

30. During saltatory conduction,
    a. action potentials move in all directions along an axon
    b. action potentials occur at successive nodes along the length of the stimulated axon
    c. local currents depolarize adjacent areas of membrane so that action potentials continue to form along the membrane
    d. action potentials produce a local current that is strong enough to spread along the length of the axon
    e. local potentials produce a continuous outward flow of potassium ions

    Answer: b

31. Which type of synapse dominates the nervous system?
    a. chemical
    b. electrical
    c. mechanical
    d. processing
    e. radioactive

    Answer: a

32. The ion needed to initiate the release of acetylcholine into the synaptic cleft is
    a. sodium
    b. potassium
    c. calcium
    d. chloride
    e. zinc

    Answer: c

33. Cholinergic synapses release the neurotransmitter
    a. norepinephrine
    b. adrenalin
    c. serotonin
    d. acetylcholine
    e. GABA

    Answer: d

34. Adrenergic synapses release the neurotransmitter
    a. acetylcholine
    b. norepinephrine
    c. dopamine
    d. serotonin
    e. GABA

    Answer: b

35. Neurons normally derive ATP solely through
    a. aerobic respiration
    b. anaerobic respiration
    c. formation of creatine phosphate
    d. use of stored glycogen
    e. a and d

    Answer: a

36. A group of interconnected neurons with specific functions is called a
    a. discharge pool
    b. neuronal pool
    c. neuronal zone
    d. facilitated zone
    e. facilitated group

    Answer: b

37. The processing of the same information at the same time by several neuronal pools is called
    a. serial processing
    b. parallel processing
    c. divergent processing
    d. convergent processing
    e. facilitation

    Answer: b

38. Neural reflexes
    a. are automatic motor responses
    b. are triggered by specific stimuli
    c. help preserve homeostasis
    d. show little variability in response
    e. all of the above

    Answer: e

39. The following are the steps involved in a reflex arc
    1. activation of a sensory neuron
    2. activation of a motor neuron
    3. response by an effector
    4. arrival of a stimulus and activation of a receptor
    5. information processing

    The proper sequence of these steps is:
    a. 1, 3, 4, 5, 2
    b. 4, 5, 3, 1, 2
    c. 4, 1, 5, 2, 3
    d. 4, 3, 1, 5, 2
    e. 3, 1, 4, 5, 2

    Answer: c

40. The specialized membranes that protect the spinal cord are termed
    a. cranial meninges
    b. cranial mater
    c. spinal meninges
    d. spinal mater
    e. epidural membranes

    Answer: c

41. Blood vessels servicing the spinal cord are found in the
    a. pia mater
    b. dura mater
    c. epidural space
    d. subdural space
    e. subarachnoid space

    Answer: a

42. The following are the "layers" of meninges
    1. subarachnoid space
    2. pia mater
    3. arachnoid mater
    4. epidural space
    5. dura mater

    The correct order superficial to deep is:
    a. 1, 3, 2, 5, 4
    b. 4, 5, 3, 2, 1
    c. 4, 5, 3, 1, 2
    d. 5, 4, 3, 1, 2
    e. 3, 2, 4, 5, 1

    Answer: c

43. The glial cells responsible for maintaining the blood-brain barrier are the
    a. astrocytes
    b. Schwann cells
    c. microglia
    d. ependymal cells
    e. fiber cells

Answer: a

44. The projections of gray matter toward the outer surface of the spinal cord are called
    a. wings
    b. horns
    c. pyramids
    d. fibers
    e. tracts

Answer: b

45. Each of the following statements concerning the gray matter of the spinal cord is true **except** one. Identify the exception.
    a. The gray matter is located in the interior of the spinal cord around the central canal.
    b. The gray matter functions in processing neural information.
    c. The gray matter is primarily involved in relaying information to the brain.
    d. The gray matter contains motor neurons.
    e. The gray matter is divided into regions called horns.

Answer: c

46. Axons crossing from one side of the spinal cord to the other within the gray matter are found in the
    a. anterior gray horns
    b. lateral gray horns
    c. posterior gray horns
    d. gray commissures
    e. white commissures

Answer: d

47. The white matter of the spinal cord contains
    a. bundles of axons that share common origins, destinations, and functions
    b. bundles of dendrites that share common origins, destinations, and functions
    c. sensory and motor nuclei
    d. both axons and dendrites
    e. interneurons

Answer: a

48. A deep crease along the ventral surface of the spinal cord forms the
    a. anterior median sulcus
    b. posterior median sulcus
    c. anterior median fissure
    d. posterior median fissure
    e. spinal cord terminus

Answer: c

49. Enlargements of the spinal cord occur
    a. near the posterior median sulcus
    b. adjacent to the anterior median fissure
    c. in segments of the spinal cord that control the limbs
    d. in the thoracic region of the spinal cord
    e. none of the above

Answer: c

50. The entire spinal cord is divided into _____ segments.
    a. 5
    b. 12
    c. 25
    d. 31
    e. 35

Answer: d

51. The adult spinal cord extends only to which vertebral level?
    a. coccyx
    b. sacral
    c. third or fourth lumbar
    d. first or second lumbar
    e. last thoracic

Answer: d

52. Which of the following link the cerebral hemispheres with the brain stem?
    a. medulla oblongata
    b. pons
    c. midbrain
    d. diencephalon
    e. cerebellum

Answer: d

53. The walls of the diencephalon form the
    a. hypothalamus
    b. thalamus
    c. brain stem
    d. midbrain
    e. cerebellum

    Answer: b

54. The tracts that connect the cerebellum to the brain stem are located in the
    a. medulla oblongata
    b. pons
    c. midbrain
    d. diencephalon
    e. thalamus

    Answer: b

55. Major centers concerned with autonomic control of breathing, blood pressure, heart rate, and digestive activities are located in the
    a. medulla oblongata
    b. pons
    c. midbrain
    d. diencephalon
    e. cerebellum

    Answer: a

56. A neural cortex is found on the surface of the
    a. cerebrum
    b. midbrain
    c. cerebellum
    d. pons
    e. both a and c

    Answer: e

57. The diencephalic chamber is called the
    a. lateral ventricle
    b. second ventricle
    c. mesencephalic aqueduct
    d. third ventricle
    e. fourth ventricle

    Answer: d

58. The ventricle associated with the pons and upper medulla is
    a. first
    b. second
    c. third
    d. fourth
    e. lateral

Answer: d

59. The dural sinuses are located in the
    a. dura mater
    b. arachnoid
    c. pia mater
    d. cortex
    e. subarachnoid space

Answer: a

60. What structure is highly vascular and closely adheres to the surface of the brain?
    a. pia mater
    b. arachnoid
    c. dura mater
    d. cortex
    e. choroid plexus

Answer: a

61. What contains a delicate network of collagen and elastin fibers through which cerebrospinal fluid circulates?
    a. epidural space
    b. dural sinus
    c. arachnoid villi
    d. subarachnoid space
    e. pia mater

Answer: d

62. Which of the following is not a function of cerebrospinal fluid?
    a. provides cushioning for delicate neural tissues
    b. provides buoyant support for the brain
    c. acts as a transport medium for nutrients
    d. provides a medium for nerve impulse transmission
    e. acts as a transport medium for chemical messengers

Answer: d

63. Which of the following is the site of cerebrospinal fluid production?
    a. dural sinus
    b. choroid plexus
    c. cortex
    d. cerebellum
    e. sagittal fissure

Answer: b

64. Diffusion across the arachnoid villi returns excess CSF to
    a. the third ventricle
    b. arterial circulation
    c. venous circulation
    d. the fourth ventricle
    e. the central canal

Answer: c

65. The two cerebral hemispheres are separated by the
    a. longitudinal fissure
    b. central sulcus
    c. lateral sulcus
    d. frontal lobe
    e. postcentral sulcus

Answer: a

66. Divisions of the cerebral hemispheres that are named after the overlying skull bones are called
    a. fissures
    b. sinuses
    c. lobes
    d. sulci
    e. gyri

Answer: c

67. The area anterior to the central sulcus is the
    a. parietal lobe
    b. temporal lobe
    c. frontal lobe
    d. occipital lobe
    e. postcentral gyrus

Answer: c

68. The cortex inferior to the lateral sulcus is the
    a. parietal lobe
    b. temporal lobe
    c. frontal lobe
    d. occipital lobe
    e. cerebellar lobe

    Answer: b

69. The primary motor cortex is located in the region of the
    a. cerebellum
    b. precentral gyrus
    c. postcentral gyrus
    d. midbrain
    e. corpus callosum

    Answer: b

70. The surface of the postcentral gyrus contains the
    a. primary sensory cortex
    b. primary motor cortex
    c. visual cortex
    d. olfactory cortex
    e. auditory cortex

    Answer: a

71. The visual cortex is located in the
    a. frontal lobe
    b. parietal lobe
    c. temporal lobe
    d. occipital lobe
    e. cerebellum

    Answer: d

72. The auditory cortex is located in the
    a. frontal lobe
    b. parietal lobe
    c. temporal lobe
    d. occipital lobe
    e. cerebellum

    Answer: c

73. Regions of the brain that are involved in interpreting data or coordinating motor responses are
    a. commissural areas
    b. sensory areas
    c. association areas
    d. motor areas
    e. processing areas

    Answer: c

74. The region of the brain that is involved in conscious thought and intellectual function as well as processing somatic sensory and motor information is the
    a. medulla
    b. pons
    c. midbrain
    d. cerebellum
    e. cerebrum

    Answer: e

75. The major communication between cerebral hemispheres occurs through the
    a. corpus spongiosum
    b. prefrontal gyrus
    c. corpus callosum
    d. postcentral gyrus
    e. hypothalamus

    Answer: c

76. Stimulation of the reticular formation results in
    a. sleep
    b. increased consciousness
    c. coma
    d. decreased cerebral function
    e. none of the above

    Answer: b

77. The _____ acts as a switching and relay center for integration of conscious and unconscious sensory and motor pathways.
    a. cerebellum
    b. midbrain
    c. diencephalon
    d. pons
    e. medulla

    Answer: c

78. Efferent tracts from the hypothalamus
    a. control involuntary motor activities
    b. control autonomic function
    c. coordinate activities of the nervous and endocrine systems
    d. a and b only
    e. all of the above

Answer: e

79. The motor nerve tracts that link the cerebellum with the brain stem are contained within the
    a. precentral gyrus
    b. postcentral gyrus
    c. cerebellar peduncles
    d. hypothalamus
    e. cerebral peduncles

Answer: c

80. Overseeing the postural muscles of the body and making rapid adjustments to maintain balance and equilibrium are functions of the
    a. cerebrum
    b. midbrain
    c. cerebellum
    d. pons
    e. medulla

Answer: c

81. The pons contains
    a. sensory and motor nuclei for six cranial nerves
    b. nuclei concerned with the control of blood pressure
    c. tracts that link the cerebellum with the brain stem
    d. no ascending or descending tracts
    e. all of the above

Answer: c

82. The horns of the spinal cord contain
    a. nerve tracts
    b. columns
    c. meninges
    d. nerve cell bodies
    e. all of the above

Answer: d

83. The posterior horns of the spinal cord contain
    a. sensory nuclei
    b. somatic motor nuclei
    c. autonomic motor nuclei
    d. nerve tracts
    e. all of the above

    Answer: a

84. The anterior horns of the spinal cord contain
    a. sensory nuclei
    b. somatic motor nuclei
    c. autonomic motor nuclei
    d. nerve tracts
    e. all of the above

    Answer: b

85. Bundles of axons in the spinal cord are called
    a. nerves
    b. tracts
    c. centers
    d. nuclei
    e. ganglia

    Answer: b

86. Most neurons lack centrosomes. This observation explains
    a. why neurons grow such long axons
    b. why neurons cannot regenerate
    c. the conducting ability of neurons
    d. the ability of neurons to communicate with each other
    e. the ability of neurons to live long lives

    Answer: b

87. Damage to large numbers of oligodendrocytes in the CNS would result in
    a. loss of the structural framework of the brain
    b. a breakdown of the blood-brain barrier
    c. inability to produce scar tissue at the site of an injury
    d. decreased production of cerebrospinal fluid
    e. decreased speed of action potential conduction

    Answer: e

88. If the sodium-potassium pumps in the cell membrane fail to function,
   a. the extracellular concentration of potassium ions will increase
   b. the intracellular concentration of sodium ions will increase
   c. the membrane will lose its capacity to generate action potentials
   d. the inside of the membrane will have a resting potential that is more positive than normal
   e. all of the above

   Answer: e

89. Ascending tracts
   a. carry sensory information to the brain
   b. carry motor information to the brain
   c. carry sensory information from the brain
   d. carry motor information from the brain
   e. none of the above

   Answer: a

90. Tracts would be found in the
   a. central canal
   b. posterior gray horns
   c. gray commissures
   d. white columns
   e. all of the above

   Answer: d

91. If the dorsal root of a spinal nerve is severed,
   a. motor control of skeletal muscles would be impaired
   b. motor control of visceral organs would be impaired
   c. the spinal cord would not be able to process information at that level
   d. the brain would not be able to communicate with that level of the spinal cord
   e. incoming sensory information would be disrupted

   Answer: e

92. In which of the following would the delay between stimulus and response be greater?
   a. a reflex that involves many synapses
   b. a reflex that involves fewer synapses

   Answer: a

93. Mike's father suffers a stroke that leaves him partially paralyzed on his right side. What type of glial cell would you expect to find in increased numbers in the area of his brain that is damaged by the stroke?
    a. astrocytes
    b. Schwann cells
    c. oligodendrocytes
    d. microglia
    e. ependymal cells

    Answer: d

94. Tetradotoxin is a toxin that blocks the sodium channels from opening. What effect would this have on the function of neurons?
    a. neurons would depolarize more rapidly
    b. action potentials would lack a repolarization phase
    c. the refractory period would be shorter than normal
    d. the neurons would not be able to propagate action potentials
    e. none of the above

    Answer: d

95. After suffering a stroke, Cindy finds that she cannot move her right arm. This would suggest that the stroke damage is in the area of the
    a. right frontal lobe
    b. left frontal lobe
    c. right temporal lobe
    d. left temporal lobe
    e. occipital lobe

    Answer: b

96. After suffering a blow to the back of the head, Phil becomes comatose. The blow probably caused damage to the:
    a. precentral gyrus
    b. postcentral gyrus
    c. hypothalamus
    d. limbic system
    e. reticular formation

    Answer: e

97. The following is a series of events that occur at a typical cholinergic synapse. Place the events in the correct sequence.
    1. Calcium ions enter the cytoplasm of the synaptic knob and ACh release occurs.
    2. Arriving action potential depolarizes the synaptic knob and the presynaptic membrane.
    3. Depolarization ends as ACh is broken down into acetate and choline by AChE.
    4. ACh release ceases because calcium ions are removed from the cytoplasm of the synaptic knob.
    5. The synaptic knob reabsorbs choline from the synaptic cleft and uses it to resynthesize ACh.
    6. ACH diffuses across the synaptic cleft and binds to receptors on the postsynaptic membrane.
    7. Sodium channels on postsynaptic surface are activated, producing a graded depolarization.

    The correct sequence of events is:
    a. 2, 1, 6, 7, 4, 3, 5
    b. 2, 6, 8, 1, 3, 5, 7
    c. 1, 3, 5, 7, 2, 4, 6
    d. 1, 2, 4, 5, 3, 6, 7
    e. 7, 4, 5, 6, 2, 3, 1

    Answer: a

98. Head injuries that damage cerebral blood vessels are serious conditions because
    a. it could cause severe pain
    b. these spaces compress and distort the relatively soft tissues of the brain
    c. epicardial tissue will be affected
    d. the venous sinus will not drain
    e. pathways will be blocked

    Answer: b

99. A disorder affecting the ability to speak or read is known as
    a. amnesia
    b. dyslexia
    c. aphasia
    d. apraxia
    e. hemiaplasia

    Answer: c

100. A disorder affecting the comprehension and use of words is termed
    a. amnesia
    b. aphasia
    c. apraxia
    d. dyslexia
    e. hemiaplasia

Answer: d

101. _____ refers to the loss of memory from disease or trauma.
    a. Hemiaplasia
    b. Aphasia
    c. Dyslexia
    d. Amnesia
    e. Apraxia

Answer: d

102. Seizures are frequently accompanied by
    a. involuntary movements
    b. unusual sensations
    c. inappropriate behaviors
    d. normal electroencephalograms
    e. a, b, and c

Answer: e

103. Synaptic knobs occur at the ends of
    a. dendrites
    b. somas
    c. telodendria
    d. peduncles
    e. axons

Answer: a

104. Brain waves found on an EEG in normal adults under resting conditions are
    a. theta waves
    b. alpha waves
    c. beta waved
    d. delta waves
    e. all of the above

Answer: b

105. Brain waves found on an EEG during times of stress or tension are
   a. alpha waves
   b. beta waves
   c. delta waves
   d. theta waves
   e. none of the above

   Answer: b

Matching

106. Match the term in the first column with its description in the second.

   _____1. exteroceptor
   _____2. neuroglia
   _____3. astrocytes
   _____4. dopamine
   _____5. soma

   A. neuron cell body
   B. neurotransmitter
   C. provide information about the external environment
   D. provide a supporting framework
   E. largest and most numerous type of glial cells

   Answer: 1-c, 2-d, 3-e, 4-b, 5-a

Fill-In-The-Blank

107. All of the nervous tissue outside of the central nervous system comprises the _____ nervous system.

   Answer: peripheral

108. The _____ division of the nervous system brings sensory information to the central nervous system.

   Answer: afferent

109. The _____ division of the nervous system carries motor commands to muscles and glands.

   Answer: efferent

110. The _____ nervous system provides involuntary regulation of smooth muscle, cardiac muscle and glandular activity.

   Answer: autonomic

111. The _____ of the neuron is the cell body.

   Answer: soma

112. _____ is a wrapping produced by some glial cells that is primarily lipid in constitution.

    Answer: Myelin

113. The gaps between adjacent Schwann cells along the length of an axon are called _____.

    Answer: nodes

114. The minimum amount of stimulus required to depolarize an excitable membrane and generate an action potential is known as the _____.

    Answer: threshold

115. The _____ principle states that the properties of the action potential are independent of the relative strength of the depolarizing stimulus.

    Answer: all-or-nothing

116. The time during which an excitable membrane cannot respond to further stimulation is the _____ _____.

    Answer: refractory period

117. An action potential traveling along an axon is called a(n) _____ _____.

    Answer: nerve impulse

118. At a chemical synapse, a _____ is released to stimulate the next neuron in sequence.

    Answer: neurotransmitter

119. Adrenergic neurons release the neurotransmitter, _____.

    Answer: norepinephrine

120. Cholinergic neurons release the neurotransmitter, _____.

    Answer: acetylcholine

121. The neural pathway of a single reflex is called a(n) _____ _____.

    Answer: reflex arc

122. _____ reflexes involve skeletal muscles.

    Answer: Somatic

123. _____ reflexes involve visceral organs.

    Answer: Visceral

124. The outermost layer of the meninges is the _____.

    Answer: dura mater

125. The _____ _____ is the layer of the meninges that is in direct contact with the surface of the brain.

    Answer: pia mater

126. The fluid which surrounds and bathes the central nervous system is _____ _____.

    Answer: cerebrospinal fluid or CSF

127. The histological plan of the spinal cord is _____ matter surrounded by _____ matter.

    Answer: gray; white

128. _____ are chambers within the brain that contain CSF.

    Answer: Ventricles

129. The _____ ventricle is at the level of the pons and cerebellum.

    Answer: fourth

130. The _____ ventricle is at the level of the thalamus.

    Answer: third

131. The major motor cortex of the cerebrum is located in the _____ gyrus.

    Answer: precentral

132. The major sensory cortex of the cerebrum is located in the _____ gyrus.

    Answer: postcentral

Essay

133. Meningitis is a condition in which the meninges of the brain become inflamed as the result of a viral or bacterial infection. This condition can be life threatening. Explain why.

Answer:
As in any inflamed tissue, there is edema in the area of the inflammation. The accumulation of fluid in the subarachnoid space can cause damage by pressing against the neurons. If the intracranial pressure is excessive, brain damage can occur; and if the pressure involves vital autonomic reflex areas, death could occur.

134. Kelsey falls down a flight of stairs and suffers spinal cord damage due to hyperextension of the cord during the fall. The injury results in edema of the central cord with resulting compression of the anterior horn cells of the lumbar region. What symptoms would you expect to observe as a result of this injury?

Answer:
The anterior horn cells of the spinal cord are somatic motor neurons that direct the activity of skeletal muscles. The lumbar region of the spinal cord controls the skeletal muscles that are involved with the control of the muscles of the hip, leg, and foot. As a result of the injury, Kelsey would have poor control of most leg muscles, a problem with walking if she could walk at all, and if she could stand, problems maintaining balance.

135. In multiple sclerosis, there is progressive and intermittent damage to the myelin sheath of peripheral nerves. This results in poor motor control of the affected area. Why does destruction of the myelin sheath affect motor control?

Answer:
Action potentials travel faster along fibers that are myelinated than fibers that are non-myelinated. Destruction of the myelin sheath slows the time it takes for motor neurons to communicate with their effector muscles. This delay in response results in varying degrees of uncoordinated muscle activity. The situation is very similar to a newborn where the infant cannot control its arms and legs very well because the myelin sheaths are still being laid down for the first year of life. Since not all motor neurons to the same muscle may be demyelinated to the same degree, there would be some fibers that are slow to respond while there would be others that are responding normally, thus producing contractions that are erratic and poorly controlled.

Chapter 9: The Peripheral Nervous System and Integrated Functions

Multiple Choice

1. There are _____ pairs of cranial nerves.
   a. 6
   b. 8
   c. 10
   d. 12
   e. 31

   Answer: d

2. The only cranial nerve that is attached to the cerebrum is the
   a. optic
   b. oculomotor
   c. trochlear
   d. olfactory
   e. vestibulocochlear

   Answer: d

3. The cranial nerves that are involved in controlling eye movements are
   a. I, II, and III
   b. III, IV, and VI
   c. II, III, and IV
   d. II and VI
   e. III and V

   Answer: b

4. The cranial nerve that has three branches is the
   a. abducens
   b. facial
   c. vagus
   d. trigeminal
   e. glossopharyngeal

   Answer: d

5. The cranial nerves which are primarily sensory include
   a. I, II and V
   b. I, V and VIII
   c. II, III and VIII
   d. I, II and VIII
   e. I, III and VIII

   Answer: d

6. Motor innervation of the voluntary swallowing muscles and intrinsic laryngeal muscles is by way of the
   a. abducens nerve
   b. facial nerve
   c. spinal accessory nerve
   d. trigeminal nerve
   e. vagus nerve

   Answer: c

7. Damage to which of the following cranial nerves could result in death?
   a. abducens
   b. facial
   c. glossopharyngeal
   d. vagus
   e. hypoglossal

   Answer: d

8. Which of the following pairs is not properly matched?
   a. cervical spinal nerves: 8
   b. thoracic spinal nerves: 12
   c. lumbar spinal nerves: 4
   d. sacral spinal nerves: 5
   e. coccygeal spinal nerves: 1

   Answer: c

9. Muscles of the neck and shoulder are innervated by spinal nerves from the
   a. cervical region
   b. thoracic region
   c. lumbar region
   d. sacral region
   e. coccygeal region

   Answer: a

10. Spinal nerves from the sacral region of the cord innervate
    a. the shoulder muscles
    b. the chest muscles
    c. the abdominal muscles
    d. the leg muscles
    e. c and d

    Answer: d

11. The joining of adjacent spinal nerves is termed a
    a. cranial nerve
    b. conjoined spinal nerve
    c. lateral nerve group
    d. tract
    e. plexus

Answer: e

12. The stretch reflex
    a. is an example of a polysynaptic reflex
    b. is important in regulating posture
    c. involves a receptor called the Golgi tendon organ
    d. is activated when a skeletal muscle shortens
    e. all of the above

Answer: b

13. Another name for the patellar reflex is the
    a. knee jerk reflex
    b. spinal short reflex
    c. dorsiflexion reflex
    d. long spinal reflex
    e. none of the above

Answer: a

14. Which of the following are capable of producing the more complex reflexes?
    a. monosynaptic reflexes
    b. polysynaptic reflexes

Answer: b

15. Muscle spindles
    a. are found in skeletal muscles
    b. are found within joint capsules
    c. are controlled through the cranial nerves
    d. help prevent muscle damage that would result from over stretching
    e. a and d only

Answer: e

16. The flexor reflex
    a. prevents a muscle from over stretching
    b. prevents a muscle from generating damaging tension
    c. moves a limb away from a painful stimulus
    d. makes adjustments in other parts of the body in response to a particular stimulus
    e. is an example of a monosynaptic reflex

Answer: c

17. Which of the following is responsible for reciprocal inhibition?
    a. sensory neurons
    b. motor neurons
    c. interneurons
    d. extensor neurons
    e. none of the above

    Answer: c

18. Control of spinal reflexes by the brain involves
    a. descending tracts of the spinal cord
    b. conscious control
    c. activation of the precentral gyrus
    d. thoracic and lumbar spinal nerves only
    e. all of the above

    Answer: e

19. Which of the following is abnormal in the adult?
    a. plantar reflex
    b. Babinski sign
    c. withdrawal reflex
    d. flexor reflex
    e. knee jerk reflex

    Answer: b

20. The established motor patterns for walking, running and jumping are primarily directed by neuronal pools in the
    a. precentral gyrus
    b. spinal cord
    c. cerebellum
    d. postcentral gyrus
    e. limbic system

    Answer: b

21. The simplest reflexes are mediated at the level of the
    a. cerebrum
    b. midbrain
    c. cerebellum
    d. medulla
    e. spinal cord

    Answer: e

22. The highest levels of information processing occur in the
    a. cerebrum
    b. midbrain
    c. cerebellum
    d. medulla
    e. spinal cord

Answer: a

23. The spinal tract or pathway that carries highly localized sensory
    information concerning fine touch and pressure is the
    a. spinothalamic
    b. posterior column
    c. pyramidal system
    d. extrapyramidal system
    e. spinocerebellar

Answer: b

24. The spinal tract or pathway that carries proprioceptive information is
    the
    a. posterior column
    b. spinothalamic
    c. pyramidal
    d. extrapyramidal
    e. spinocerebellar

Answer: e

25. The spinal tract or pathway that carries information regulating skeletal
    muscle tone is the
    a. posterior column
    b. spinothalamic
    c. pyramidal
    d. extrapyramidal
    e. spinocerebellar

Answer: d

26. Which of the following is a descending tract or pathway of the spinal
    cord?
    a. posterior column
    b. spinothalamic
    c. pyramidal
    d. extrapyramidal
    e. c and d only

Answer: e

27. The pyramidal system
    a. provides voluntary control over skeletal muscles
    b. provides voluntary control over smooth muscles
    c. provides involuntary control over skeletal muscles
    d. provides involuntary control over smooth muscles
    e. c and d

    Answer: a

28. Voluntary control of skeletal muscles is provided by the
    a. posterior column
    b. reticular formation
    c. spinothalamic tract
    d. pyramidal system
    e. medullary centers

    Answer: d

29. The area of sensory cortex devoted to a body region is relative to
    a. the size of the body area
    b. the distance of the body area from the brain
    c. the number of motor units in the area of the body
    d. the number of sensory receptors in the area of the body
    e. the size of the nerves that serve the area of the body

    Answer: d

30. We can distinguish between sensations that originate in different areas
    of the body because
    a. sensory neurons carry only one type of information
    b. sensory neurons from each body region synapse in specific brain
       regions
    c. incoming sensory information is first assessed by the thalamus
    d. different types of sensory receptors produce different types of
       action potentials
    e. the sensory neurons in different parts of the body are different from
       each other

    Answer: b

31. Information received by the brain concerning internal or external
    environmental conditions is called a(n)
    a. action potential
    b. effector
    c. stimulus
    d. sensation
    e. response

    Answer: d

32. Complex motor activities like riding a bicycle or eating
    a. only require neural processing at the level of the cerebrum
    b. involve little input from the brain
    c. require the coordinated activity of several regions of the brain
    d. are controlled at the level of the spinal cord
    e. do not require input from the cerebellum

    Answer: c

33. The cerebellum adjusts voluntary and involuntary motor activity in response to
    a. proprioceptive data
    b. visual information
    c. equilibrium-related sensations
    d. information from the cerebral cortex
    e. all of the above

    Answer: e

34. An autonomic motor neuron whose cell body lies in the CNS is called
    a. an upper motor neuron
    b. a lower motor neuron
    c. a preganglionic neuron
    d. a postganglionic neuron
    e. a somatic motor neuron

    Answer: c

35. The autonomic division of the nervous system directs
    a. voluntary motor activity
    b. conscious control of skeletal muscles
    c. unconscious control of skeletal muscles
    d. processes that maintain homeostasis
    e. all of the above

    Answer: d

36. In the autonomic nervous system,
    a. neurons have axons but no dendrites
    b. there is always a synapse between the CNS and the effector organ
    c. motor neurons do not synapse but are connected by gap junctions
    d. the cell bodies of all motor neurons are found in ganglia outside of the CNS
    e. neurons have dendrites but no axons

    Answer: b

37. Postganglionic fibers of autonomic neurons are usually
    a. connected to effector organs
    b. short in length
    c. larger than preganglionic fibers
    d. located in the brain
    e. located in the spinal cord

    Answer: a

38. The division of the autonomic nervous system that prepares the body for activity and stress is the
    a. sympathetic division
    b. parasympathetic division
    c. craniosacral division
    d. arachnoid division
    e. somatic motor division

    Answer: a

39. The division of the autonomic nervous system that maintains homeostasis during resting conditions is the
    a. sympathetic division
    b. parasympathetic division
    c. thoracolumbar division
    d. arachnoid division
    e. somatic motor division

    Answer: b

40. Preganglionic neurons of the sympathetic nervous system are located in the
    a. gray matter of the cervical region of the spinal cord
    b. gray matter of the cervical and thoracic region of the spinal cord
    c. gray matter of segments TI to L2 of the spinal cord
    d. gray matter of segments TI to L5 of the spinal cord
    e. gray matter of TI to S2 of the spinal cord

    Answer: c

41. Nerves that innervate organs in the ventral body cavities are the
    a. cervical spinal nerves
    b. thoracic spinal nerves
    c. cranial nerves
    d. autonomic nerves
    e. somatic motor nerves

    Answer: d

42. Each of the following effects is associated with the action of postganglionic sympathetic fibers **except** one. Identify the exception.
    a. increased sweat secretion
    b. reduced circulation to the skin
    c. decreased heart rate
    d. dilation of the pupils
    e. increased blood flow to skeletal muscles

Answer: c

43. The celiac ganglion innervates the
    a. stomach
    b. liver
    c. pancreas
    d. spleen
    e. all of the above

Answer: e

44. Sympathetic innervation of the urinary bladder and sex organs is by way of the
    a. celiac ganglion
    b. superior mesenteric ganglion
    c. optic ganglion
    d. inferior mesenteric ganglion
    e. pelvic ganglion

Answer: d

45. There are _____ sympathetic collateral ganglia located in the abdominal cavity.
    a. 1
    b. 2
    c. 3
    d. 4
    e. 6

Answer: c

46. Preganglionic fibers of parasympathetic neurons can be found in cranial nerve
    a. III
    b. VII
    c. IX
    d. X
    e. all of the above

Answer: e

47. Almost 75% of all parasympathetic outflow travels along the
    a. oculomotor nerve
    b. splanchnic nerves
    c. vagus nerve
    d. pelvic nerves
    e. collateral nerve

    Answer: c

48. Effects produced by the parasympathetic branch of the autonomic nervous system include
    a. dilation of the pupils
    b. increased secretion by digestive glands
    c. dilation of respiratory passages
    d. increased heart rate
    e. all of the above

    Answer: b

49. Increased parasympathetic stimulation
    a. increases heart rate
    b. increases the general level of activity of the digestive system
    c. causes sweat glands to release sweat
    d. causes blood vessels in the skin to dilate
    e. causes the pupils to dilate

    Answer: b

50. Dual innervation refers to
    a. an organ receiving two nerves from the spinal cord
    b. an organ receiving both autonomic and somatic motor nerves
    c. an organ receiving both sympathetic and parasympathetic nerves
    d. an organ receiving nerves from both the brain and the spinal cord
    e. none of the above

    Answer: c

51. Proper control of the respiratory passages depends upon
    a. sympathetic stimulation only
    b. parasympathetic stimulation only
    c. somatic motor stimulation only
    d. both parasympathetic and sympathetic levels of stimulation
    e. none of the above

    Answer: d

52. A decrease in the autonomic tone of the smooth muscle in blood vessels would result in
    a. an increase in vessel diameter
    b. a decrease in vessel diameter
    c. no change in vessel diameter
    d. a decrease in blood flow through the vessel
    e. increased frequency of muscle contractions

    Answer: a

53. Changes in the central nervous system that accompany aging include
    a. a reduction in brain size and weight
    b. an increase in the number of neurons
    c. an increased blood flow to the brain
    d. an increased number of synaptic connections
    e. all of the above

    Answer: a

54. Alzheimer's disease
    a. is the most common cause of senile dementia
    b. is characterized by a progressive loss of memory
    c. is characterized by a progressive loss of verbal and reading skills
    d. is associated with the formation of plaques and neurofibrillary
       tangles in regions of the brain that are involved with memory
    e. all of the above

    Answer: e

55. Injury to the neurons of a collateral ganglion would affect the function of the
    a. heart
    b. pupils
    c. sweat glands
    d. digestive system
    e. arrector pili muscles

    Answer: d

56. Damage to the ventral roots of the first five thoracic spinal nerves on the right side of the body would interfere with
    a. the ability to dilate the right pupil
    b. the ability to dilate the left pupil
    c. the ability to contract the right biceps
    d. the ability to contract the left biceps
    e. all of the above

    Answer: a

57. Stimulation of the neurons in the celiac ganglion would lead to
    a. urination
    b. increased heart rate
    c. release of glucose from the liver's glycogen reserves
    d. release of sweat from sweat glands on the upper back
    e. all of the above

    Answer: c

58. Ascending tracts
    a. carry sensory information to the brain
    b. carry motor information to the brain
    c. carry sensory information from the brain
    d. carry motor information from the brain
    e. none of the above

    Answer: a

59. During sympathetic stimulation, a person may begin to feel "on edge";
    this is the result of
    a. increased energy metabolism by muscle tissue
    b. increased cardiovascular activity
    c. stimulation of the reticular activating system
    d. temporary insensitivity to painful stimuli
    e. decreased levels of epinephrine in the blood

    Answer: c

60. Which of the following would be greater?
    a. The heart rate when sympathetic neurons are stimulated.
    b. The heart rate when parasympathetic neurons are stimulated.

    Answer: a

61. Under which set of circumstances would the diameter of peripheral blood
    vessels be the greatest?
    a. increased sympathetic stimulation
    b. decreased sympathetic stimulation
    c. increased parasympathetic stimulation
    d. decreased parasympathetic stimulation
    e. both increased parasympathetic and increased sympathetic stimulation

    Answer: b

62. This term refers to a number of disorders affecting voluntary motor performance that appear during infancy or childhood and persist throughout the life of the affected individual.
    a. muscular dystrophy
    b. multiple sclerosis
    c. polymyositis
    d. cerebral palsy
    e. cystic fibrosis

    Answer: d

63. Identify the inherited condition characterized by the progressive degeneration of neurons in the frontal lobes and cerebral nuclei.
    a. Broca's aphasia
    b. Huntington's disease
    c. Parkinson's disease
    d. Cushing's disease
    e. Addison's disease

    Answer: b

64. A progressive disorder characterized by the loss of higher cerebral functions is termed
    a. Alzheimer's disease
    b. Broca's disease
    c. Huntington's disease
    d. Parkinson's disease
    e. cerebral palsy

    Answer: a

65. Age-related changes associated with the nervous system include all of the following **except**:
    a. a reduction in brain weight and size
    b. a decrease in blood flow to the brain
    c. an increase in the number of neurons
    d. an accumulation of abnormal intracellular deposits
    e. a decrease in the number of dendritic interconnections and branchings

    Answer: c

66. A <u>sympathetic</u> innervation effect of the eye would be
    a. dilation of the pupil
    b. constriction of the pupil
    c. focusing for near vision
    d. A and C
    e. none of the above

    Answer: a

67. A <u>parasympathetic</u> innervation effect of the digestive system would be
    a. decrease in activity
    b. increase in activity
    c. glycogen catabolism
    d. glycogen synthesis
    e. B and D

    Answer: e

68. All but one of the 12 pairs of cranial nerves arise from the
    a. cerebrum
    b. cerebellum
    c. brain stem
    d. spinal cord
    e. corpus callosum

    Answer: c

69. An example of a monosynaptic reflex is the
    a. flexor reflex
    b. stretch reflex
    c. withdrawal reflex
    d. A and B
    e. none of the above

    Answer: b

Matching

70. Match the cranial nerve in the first column with its innervation in the second column.

    _____1. optic
    _____2. abducens
    _____3. facial
    _____4. accessory
    _____5. trochlear

    A. palate, pharynx, larynx, sternocleidomastoid, trapezius
    B. superior oblique muscle
    C. retina of eye
    D. lateral rectus muscle of eye
    E. taste receptors, lacrimal gland, sublingual glands

    Answer: 1-c, 2-d, 3-e, 4-a, 5-b

71. Match the plexus in the first column with its major nerve in the second column.

    _____1. cervical plexus
    _____2. brachial plexus
    _____3. lumbosacral plexus

    A. phrenic nerve
    B. obturator, femoral, gluteal, sciatic, and saphenous nerves
    C. axillary, musculocutaneous, median, radial, and ulnar nerves

    Answer: 1-a, 2-c, 3-b

Fill-In-The-Blank

72. The vagus nerve is cranial nerve _____.

    Answer: X (10)

73. The optic nerve is cranial nerve _____.

    Answer: II (2)

74. The vestibulocochlear (acoustic) nerve is cranial nerve _____.

    Answer: VIII (8)

75. A complex, interwoven network of nerves is called a(n) _____ _____.

    Answer: nerve plexus

76. The _____ nerve innervates the diaphragm.

    Answer: phrenic

77. The radial nerve arises from the _____ plexus, and functions to _____ muscles of the forearm, arm and hand.

    Answer: brachial; extend

78. Both the femoral and sciatic nerves arise from the _____ plexus.

    Answer: lumbosacral

79. The _____ pathway exercises voluntary control of skeletal muscles throughout the body.

    Answer: pyramidal

80. Information received by the brain on internal or external conditions are called _____.

    Answer: sensations

81. When visceral structures are innervated by fibers from both the sympathetic and parasympathetic divisions of the ANS, the condition is called _____ _____.

    Answer: dual innervation

82. The "rest and repose" division of the ANS is the _____.

    Answer: parasympathetic

83. The "fight or flight" division of the ANS is the _____.

    Answer: sympathetic

Essay

84. Phil had to have his arm amputated after an accident. He tells you that he can sometimes still feel pain in his fingers even though the hand is gone. He says this is especially true when he bumps the stub of his arm where it is amputated. How can this be?

    Answer:
    Phil is experiencing phantom pain. Since pain perception occurs in the sensory cortex of the brain, he can still feel pain in his fingers if the brain projects feeling to that area. When he bumps the arm at the elbow, sensory receptors are stimulated that send impulses to the sensory cortex. The brain perceives a sensation from a general area, and projects that feeling to a body part. Since more sensory information reaches the brain from the hands and fingers, it is not unusual for the brain to project to this area.

85. In some severe cases, a person suffering from stomach ulcers may have surgery to cut the branches of the vagus nerve that innervates the stomach. How would this help the problem?

    Answer:
    The vagus nerve carries motor neurons of the parasympathetic nervous system. These motor neurons control gastric secretions, notably the secretion of acid and enzymes. Severing these branches would eliminate neural stimulation from the central nervous system, thus eliminating the release of gastric fluids in response to anxiety and other higher-order stimuli when there is no food in the stomach. Normal digestive function would still occur, governed by various hormones and intramural neural reflexes.

86. A condition known as Bell's palsy is thought to be caused by an inflammation of the facial nerve (VII). What symptoms would you expect to see in a person suffering from this condition?

Answer:
Patients suffering from Bell's palsy usually experience numbness or a feeling of stiffness in the face on the affected side. Weakness of the facial muscles on the affected side may produce an inability to wrinkle the forehead, close the eye, pucker the lips or retract the mouth. Other possible symptoms include loss of taste sensations, reduction in the amount of saliva from the salivary glands of the affected side, pain behind the ear, ringing sensation in the ear or possibly some hearing loss.

Chapter 10:   Sensory Function

Multiple Choice

1. The term general senses refers to sensations of
   a. hot and cold
   b. pain
   c. touch and vibration
   d. b and c
   e. all of the above

   Answer: e

2. The special senses are
   a. olfaction
   b. vision
   c. gustation
   d. equilibrium
   e. all of the above

   Answer: e

3. The general senses
   a. involve receptors that are relatively simple
   b. are located in specialized structures called sense organs
   c. localized in specific areas of the body
   d. do not conduct action potentials
   e. a and c

   Answer: a

4. Our perception of our environment is incomplete because
   a. humans do not have receptors for every possible stimulus
   b. our receptors have ranges of sensitivity
   c. all of our awareness of the environment must be learned
   d. a and b only
   e. all of the above

   Answer: d

5. Only about _____ percent of the information provided by afferent fibers reaches the cerebral cortex and conscious awareness.
   a. 1
   b. 3
   c. 5
   d. 8
   e. 12

   Answer: a

6. Adaptation is defined as
   a. a reduction in sensitivity in the presence of a constant stimulus
   b. an increase in sensitivity in the presence of a constant stimulus

   Answer: a

7. Nociceptors are sensitive to
   a. pain
   b. light touch
   c. pressure
   d. osmotic pressure
   e. blood pressure

   Answer: a

8. The perception of pain coming from parts of the body that are not actually stimulated is called
   a. preferential pain
   b. recalcitrant pain
   c. actual pain
   d. referred pain
   e. slow pain

   Answer: d

9. Thermoreceptors
   a. are scattered immediately below the surface of the skin
   b. respond to changes in heat or cold
   c. are free nerve endings incapable of adapting
   d. a and b
   e. all of the above

   Answer: d

10. Sensory receptors that monitor the position of joints are called
    a. nociceptors
    b. chemoreceptors
    c. baroreceptors
    d. proprioceptors
    e. thermoreceptors

    Answer: d

11. Sensory receptors that respond to changes in blood pressure are called
    a. nociceptors
    b. baroreceptors
    c. chemoreceptors
    d. proprioceptors
    e. thermoreceptors

    Answer: b

12. Tactile receptors provide sensations for all of the following **except**
    a. vibration
    b. touch
    c. light touch
    d. pain
    e. pressure

Answer: d

13. Chemoreceptors are located in the
    a. carotid and aortic bodies
    b. special senses of taste and smell
    c. respiratory control center of the medulla
    d. a and b only
    e. all of the above

Answer: e

14. Olfactory glands
    a. contain the neural receptors for the sense of smell
    b. form the basement membrane of the olfactory epithelium
    c. are sensitive to aromatic molecules in the air
    d. produce a pigmented mucus that covers the olfactory epithelium
    e. form structures called olfactory bulbs

Answer: d

15. The mucus that covers the olfactory epithelium
    a. prevents the buildup of potentially dangerous stimuli
    b. keeps the tissue moist
    c. keeps the tissue free of dirt and debris
    d. provides a medium in which water-soluble molecules in the air can dissolve
    e. all of the above

Answer: e

16. Which of the following concerning olfaction is false?
    a. Olfactory receptors are highly modified neurons.
    b. Molecules to be smelled must first dissolve in the mucus covering the olfactory receptors.
    c. Humans may have as many as 20 million olfactory receptors.
    d. Human power of olfaction is as powerful as most other mammals.
    e. Olfactory stimuli do not pass through the thalamus before journeying to the olfactory cortex.

Answer: d

17. The only known example of neuronal replacement in the adult human involves the
    a. gustatory receptors
    b. nociceptors
    c. pain receptors
    d. olfactory receptors
    e. retinal cells

Answer: d

18. Gustatory receptors are located
    a. in the eye
    b. in the ear
    c. on the tongue's surface
    d. in the nose
    e. on the skin

Answer: c

19. There are _____ primary taste sensations.
    a. 2
    b. 4
    c. 12
    d. 20
    e. more than 50

Answer: b

20. Taste buds are monitored by cranial nerves
    a. IX, X, XI
    b. VII, VIII, IX
    c. VII, IX, X
    d. V, VII, IX
    e. IX, XI, XII

Answer: c

21. The sensory portion of the gustatory organ is (are) the
    a. taste pores
    b. taste hairs
    c. taste buds
    d. papillae
    e. supporting cells

Answer: b

22. The lacrimal glands
    a. are located in pockets in the frontal bones
    b. produce most of the volume of tears
    c. produce a slightly acidic secretion that contains lysozyme
    d. a and b only
    e. all of the above

    Answer: d

23. The fibrous tunic of the eye
    a. consists of the sclera and the cornea
    b. provides mechanical support and some protection for the eye
    c. serves as a point of attachment for extrinsic eye muscles
    d. a and c only
    e. all of the above

    Answer: e

24. The vascular tunic of the eye
    a. provides a route for blood vessels and lymphatics that supply tissues
       of the eye
    b. regulates the amount of light entering the eye
    c. secretes and reabsorbs the aqueous humor
    d. a and c only
    e. all of the above

    Answer: e

25. Which of the following extrinsic eye muscles is responsible for enabling
    the eye to look upward?
    a. inferior rectus
    b. medial rectus
    c. superior rectus
    d. inferior oblique
    e. superior oblique

    Answer: c

26. Which of the following extrinsic eye muscles is responsible for rotating
    the eye laterally?
    a. inferior rectus
    b. inferior oblique
    c. lateral rectus
    d. medial rectus
    e. superior rectus

    Answer: c

27. The free margins of the upper and lower eyelids are connected by the
    a. lateral rectus muscle
    b. canthus
    c. lacrimal caruncle
    d. sclera
    e. conjunctiva

    Answer: b

28. A structure that is located at the medial canthus and contains glands
    that produce a gritty secretion is the
    a. superior eye lid
    b. lacrimal caruncle
    c. conjunctiva
    d. tear gland
    e. schlera

    Answer: b

29. The vitreous body
    a. contains the lens
    b. helps to stabilize the eye and give physical support to the retina
    c. contains blood vessels that nourish the retina
    d. is located between the lens and the iris
    e. all of the above

    Answer: b

30. The lining of the visible outer surface of the eye is the
    a. conjunctiva
    b. cornea
    c. iris
    d. canthus
    e. pupil

    Answer: a

31. The transparent portion of the eye is the
    a. conjunctiva
    b. cornea
    c. iris
    d. pupil
    e. canthus

    Answer: b

32. The pigmented portion of the eye is the
    a. conjunctiva
    b. cornea
    c. iris
    d. pupil
    e. canthus

    Answer: c

33. The central opening in the eye through which light passes is the
    a. conjunctiva
    b. iris
    c. pupil
    d. lacrima
    e. canthus

    Answer: c

34. The space between the iris and the cornea is the
    a. anterior chamber
    b. posterior chamber
    c. pupil
    d. aqueous humor
    e. vitreous body

    Answer: a

35. The space between the suspensory ligaments and the iris is the
    a. anterior chamber
    b. posterior chamber
    c. pupil
    d. vitreous body
    e. posterior cavity

    Answer: b

36. The neural tunic
    a. consists of three distinct layers
    b. contains the photoreceptor cells
    c. produces the vitreous humor
    d. forms the iris
    e. all of the above

    Answer: b

37. The lens focuses light on the photoreceptor cells by
    a. moving up and down
    b. moving in and out
    c. changing shape
    d. opening and closing
    e. dilating and constricting

    Answer: c

38. The shape of the lens is controlled by the
    a. pupillary constrictor muscles
    b. pupillary dilator muscles
    c. ciliary muscles
    d. suspensory ligaments
    e. aqueous body

    Answer: d

39. In the human eye, the greatest amount of refraction occurs when light
    passes from the air into the
    a. iris
    b. cornea
    c. lens
    d. aqueous humor
    e. vitreous humor

    Answer: b

40. The ciliary muscle helps to
    a. control the amount of light reaching the retina
    b. control the shape of the lens
    c. control the production of aqueous humor
    d. move the eyeball
    e. a and b

    Answer: b

41. There are three different types of cones, each one sensitive to a
    different color wavelength of light. These cones are designated
    a. red, yellow, blue
    b. red, blue, green
    c. red, green, yellow
    d. yellow, green, blue
    e. red, yellow, indigo

    Answer: b

42. An area of the retina that contains only cones and is the site of
    sharpest vision is the
    a. outer segment
    b. inner segment
    c. fovea
    d. optic disk
    e. iris

    Answer: c

43. A conical outer segment composed on in-foldings of the cell membrane
    that form discs and a narrow connecting stalk that attaches the outer
    segment to the inner segment describes
    a. a bipolar cell
    b. a rod
    c. a cone
    d. an amacrine cell
    e. a horizontal cell

    Answer: c

44. When all three cone populations are stimulated one sees
    a. red
    b. blue
    c. green
    d. white
    e. black

    Answer: d

45. A blind spot in the retina occurs where
    a. the fovea is located
    b. ganglion cells synapse with bipolar cells
    c. the optic nerve attaches to the retina
    d. rod cells are clustered to form the macula
    e. amacrine cells are located

    Answer: c

46. Light absorption requires the presence of
    a. rods
    b. cones
    c. visual pigments
    d. sodium pumps
    e. neurotransmitters

    Answer: c

47. Each of the following statements concerning vision is true **except** one. Identify the exception.
    a. Approximately half of the fibers in each optic nerve cross to opposite sides of the brain at the optic chiasm.
    b. Fibers of the optic nerve synapse at the lateral geniculates of the thalamus.
    c. The image that is formed on the retina is inverted.
    d. Depth perception is improved when one eye is closed.
    e. The visual cortex of the brain contains a sensory map of the field of vision.

    Answer: d

48. The daily day/night cycle known as a circadian rhythm is established in the
    a. lateral geniculates
    b. medial geniculates
    c. pineal gland
    d. hypothalamus
    e. both a and c

    Answer: e

49. There are ____ semicircular canals in the inner ear.
    a. 2
    b. 3
    c. 4
    d. 5
    e. none of the above

    Answer: b

50. The sensory receptors of the semicircular canals are located in the
    a. saccules
    b. ampullae
    c. cristae
    d. utricles
    e. a and d

    Answer: b

51. Movement of the sensory receptors in the ampullae of the semicircular canals
    a. produces sound
    b. allows us to hear sounds
    c. stimulates the receptor cells alerting us to rotational movement
    d. stimulates the receptor cells to a change in body position with respect to gravity
    e. allows us to perceive linear acceleration

    Answer: c

52. The sensory receptor cells of the utricle and saccule are clustered in the
    a. ampullae
    b. cristae
    c. cupula
    d. maculae
    e. otoconia

Answer: d

53. The branch of the cranial nerve which is responsible for monitoring changes in equilibrium is the _____ branch.
    a. otoconial
    b. cochlear
    c. vestibular
    d. trigeminal
    e. auditory

Answer: c

54. Which descending pathway in the spinal cord is responsible for carrying reflex information maintaining postural muscle tone?
    a. vestibulospinal
    b. pyramidal
    c. extrapyramidal
    d. posterior column
    e. spinocerebellar

Answer: a

55. The following is a list of the steps that occur in the production of an auditory sensation.
    1. The pressure wave distorts the basilar membrane on its way to the round window.
    2. Movement of the tympanic membrane causes displacement of the malleus.
    3. Displacement of the stereocilia stimulates sensory neurons of the cochlear nerve.
    4. Movement of the malleus causes movement of the incus and stapes.
    5. Distortion of the basilar membrane forces the hair cells of the organ of Corti toward or away from the tectorial membrane.
    6. Movement of the oval window establishes pressure waves in the perilymph of the vestibular duct.

    The proper sequence for these steps is
    a. 2,4,1,6,5,3
    b. 2,4,6,3,5,1
    c. 2,1,4,6,5,3
    d. 2,4,6,1,5,3
    e. 2,5,4,6,1,3

Answer: d

56. The ossicles connect the
    a. tympanic membrane to the oval window
    b. tympanic membrane to the round window
    c. oval window to the round window
    d. cochlea to the tympanic membrane
    e. cochlea to the oval window

    Answer: a

57. Sound waves are converted into mechanical movements by the
    a. auditory ossicles
    b. cochlea
    c. oval window
    d. round window
    e. tympanic membrane

    Answer: e

58. The vibrations received by the ear are amplified by the action of the
    a. auditory ossicles
    b. cochlea
    c. oval window
    d. round window
    e. tympanic membrane

    Answer: a

59. A structure that allows the middle ear to communicate with the nasopharynx is the
    a. pinna
    b. vestibular duct
    c. tympanic duct
    d. Eustachian tube
    e. auditory meatus

    Answer: d

60. The sense of hearing is provided by receptors of the
    a. outer ear
    b. middle ear
    c. inner ear
    d. pinna
    e. semicircular canals

    Answer: c

61. The basic receptors in the inner ear are the
    a. utricles
    b. saccules
    c. hair cells
    d. supporting cells
    e. ampullae

    Answer: c

62. The structure that overlies the organ of Corti is the
    a. basilar membrane
    b. tectorial membrane
    c. endolymph
    d. malleus
    e. vestibular duct

    Answer: b

63. The structure that separates the cochlear duct from the tympanic duct is the
    a. tectorial membrane
    b. basilar membrane
    c. vestibular duct
    d. organ of Corti
    e. malleus

    Answer: b

64. What we perceive as the pitch of a sound is our sensory response to its
    a. amplitude
    b. wavelength
    c. frequency
    d. intensity
    e. duration

    Answer: c

65. The frequency of a sound is indicated to the nervous system by the
    a. frequency of hair cell vibration
    b. number of rows of hair cells that are stimulated
    c. region of the organ of Corti that is stimulated
    d. movement of the perilymph in the cochlear duct
    e. frequency of vibration of the tectorial membrane

    Answer: c

66. A viral infection involving the vestibular nuclei may result in
    a. loss of hearing
    b. loss of sight
    c. a sense of dizziness
    d. local paralysis
    e. high blood pressure

Answer: c

67. In which of the following situations would the pressure applied to the oval window by the stapes be the greatest?
    a. a shout
    b. a whisper

Answer: a

68. A sudden flash of bright light would
    a. cause contraction of the pupillary constrictor muscles
    b. cause contraction of the pupillary dilator muscles
    c. cause relaxation of the ciliary body
    d. cause relaxation of the ciliary ligaments
    e. increase the size of the iris

Answer: a

69. When viewing an object close to you, your lens should be
    a. more rounded
    b. more flattened
    c. more convex
    d. more lateral
    e. more medial

Answer: a

70. Damage to the fovea of the eye would interfere with the ability to
    a. focus an image
    b. regulate the amount of light striking the retina
    c. bleach visual pigments
    d. see black and white
    e. see color

Answer: e

71. A device that monitors the activity of the photoreceptor cells of the eye indicates that there is a constant flow of neurotransmitter being released by the photoreceptor cells. This information implies that the subject is
    a. reading
    b. in a dark room
    c. outside in sunlight
    d. in a brightly lit auditorium
    e. focusing on a distant object

    Answer: b

72. Your friend Shelly suffers from myopia (nearsightedness). You remember from your physics class that concave lenses cause light waves to converge and convex lenses spread light waves. What type of corrective lenses would you suggest to your friend?
    a. concave lenses
    b. convex lens

    Answer: b

73. The function of gustatory receptors parallels that of
    a. light receptors in the eye
    b. mechanoreceptors in the ear
    c. olfactory receptors in the nose
    d. nociceptors
    e. baroreceptors

    Answer: c

74. Visual acuity is also known as
    a. nearsightedness
    b. farsightedness
    c. myopia
    d. astigmatism
    e. clarity of vision

    Answer: e

75. Factors associated with blindness include all of the following **except**:
    a. diabetes mellitus
    b. myopia
    c. retinal detachment
    d. heredity
    e. glaucoma

    Answer: b

76. Loss of lens transparency is referred to as:
    a. cataract
    b. glaucoma
    c. myopia
    d. accommodation
    e. corneal scarring

Answer: a

77. Normal eye focusing is termed
    a. hyperopia
    b. myopia
    c. presbyopia
    d. emmetropia
    e. refraction

Answer: d

78. Night blindness can be treated by administering
    a. vitamin A
    b. vitamin D
    c. vitamin E
    d. vitamin K
    e. vitamin C

Answer: a

79. _____ deafness results from conditions in the middle ear that block the normal transfer of vibrations from the tympanum to the oval window.
    a. Nerve
    b. Corti
    c. Conduction
    d. Tunnel
    e. Cochlear

Answer: c .

80. Visual pigments include:
    a. rhodopsin
    b. opsin
    c. retinal
    d. A and B
    e. A, B, and C

Answer: e

Matching

81. Match the muscle in the first column with its insertion in the second column.

    _____1. inferior rectus   A. superior, lateral surface of eyeball
    _____2. superior rectus   B. inferior, lateral surface of eyeball
    _____3. inferior oblique   C. inferior, medial surface of eyeball
    _____4. superior oblique   D. lateral surface of eyeball
    _____5. lateral rectus   E. superior, medial surface of eyeball

Answer: 1-c, 2-a, 3-b, 4-e, 5-d

82. Match the muscle in the first column with its action in the second column.

    _____1. inferior rectus   A. eye looks down
    _____2. inferior oblique   B. eye rotates medially
    _____3. lateral rectus   C. eye rolls, looks up and to the side
    _____4. medial rectus   D. eye rolls, looks down and to the side
    _____5. superior oblique   E. eye rotates laterally

Answer: 1-a, 2-c, 3-e, 4-b, 5-d

Fill-In-The-Blank

83. The _____ _____ contains supporting cells and olfactory receptors.

Answer: olfactory epithelium

84. Gustatory receptors are clustered in individual _____ _____.

Answer: taste buds

85. Each gustatory cell extends a(n) _____ into the surrounding fluids through a narrow taste pore.

Answer: taste hair

86. Taste organs lie along the sides of epithelial projections called _____.

Answer: papillae

87. A _____ is an abnormal lens that has lost its clarity.

Answer: cataract

88. Persons unable to distinguish certain colors have a form of _____ _____.

    Answer: color blindness

89. _____ cells connect photoreceptors to ganglion cells.

    Answer: Bipolar

90. When light passes between media of different densities it is bent or _____.

    Answer: refracted

91. The visual receptors of the retina are called _____ and _____.

    Answer: rods; cones

92. A person suffering from _____ can see objects that are close, but distant objects appear blurred.

    Answer: myopia

93. A person suffering from _____ can see distant objects more clearly than those that are close.

    Answer: hyperopia

94. The sensory hair cells of the cochlear duct are located in the _____ _____ _____.

    Answer: organ of Corti

Essay

95. Tom has surgery to remove some polyps (growths) from his sinuses. After he heals from the surgery, he notices that his sense of smell is as keen as it was before the surgery. Can you suggest a reason for this?

    Answer:
    In removing the polyps, some of the olfactory epithelium was probably damaged or destroyed. This would decrease the area available for the solution containing odor molecules and thus the intensity of the stimulus. As a result, it would take a larger stimulus to provide the same level of smell after the surgery than before the surgery.

Chapter 11: The Endocrine System

Multiple Choice

1. The nervous system
   a. produces rapid and specific responses to environmental stimuli
   b. communicates by the release of neurotransmitters
   c. continues to produce a response long after neural output ceases
   d. a and b only
   e. all of the above

   Answer: d

2. The endocrine system
   a. releases chemicals into the bloodstream for distribution throughout the body
   b. releases hormones that alter the metabolic activities of many different tissues and organs simultaneously
   c. produces effects that can last for hours, days and even longer
   d. a and c only
   e. all of the above

   Answer: e

3. Endocrine cells
   a. are a type of nerve cell
   b. release their secretions onto an epithelial surface
   c. release their secretions into the blood
   d. contain very few vesicles
   e. all of the above

   Answer: c

4. Peptide hormones
   a. are composed by amino acids
   b. are produced by cells in the adrenal glands
   c. are derived from the amino acid tyrosine
   d. are lipids
   e. are chemically related to cholesterol

   Answer: a

5. Steroid hormones
   a. are lipids
   b. are structurally similar to cholesterol
   c. bind to cell surface receptors
   d. a and b only
   e. all of the above

   Answer: d

6. Steroid hormones
   a. are proteins
   b. cannot diffuse through cell membranes
   c. bind to receptors in the nucleus of their target cells
   d. remain in circulation for relatively short periods of time
   e. are transported in the blood dissolved in the plasma

Answer: c

7. When a protein or peptide hormone binds to receptors on the surface of a cell
   a. the hormone receptor complex moves into the cytoplasm
   b. the cell membrane becomes depolarized
   c. a second messenger appears in the cytoplasm
   d. the cell becomes inactive
   e. the hormone is transported to the nucleus where it alters the activity of DNA

Answer: c

8. Steroid hormones
   a. bind to receptors on the surface of the cell
   b. function by way of a second messenger system
   c. cannot diffuse through the cell membrane
   d. bind to intracellular receptors
   e. function by activating cAMP

Answer: d

9. A cell's hormonal sensitivities are determined by
   a. the chemical nature of the hormone
   b. the quantity of circulating hormone
   c. the shape of the hormone molecules
   d. the presence or absence of appropriate receptor complexes
   e. the thickness of the cell membrane

Answer: d

10. An important second messenger in hormonal action is
    a. cAMP
    b. ATP
    c. adenylate cyclase
    d. calcium
    e. ADP

Answer: a

11. When adenylate cyclase is activated
    a. calcium ions are released from intracellular stores
    b. cAMP is formed
    c. cAMP is broken down
    d. protein kinases are metabolized
    e. steroids are produced

    Answer: b

12. When steroid hormones bind to their receptors
    a. adenylate cyclase is activated
    b. cyclic nucleotides are formed
    c. ATP production are inhibited
    d. gene transcription occurs
    e. a and d

    Answer: d

13. The most complex endocrine responses involve the
    a. thyroid gland
    b. pancreas
    c. adrenal glands
    d. hypothalamus
    e. thymus

    Answer: d

14. Endocrine organs can be controlled by
    a. hormones from other endocrine glands
    b. releasing hormones from the hypothalamus
    c. direct neural stimulation
    d. a and c only
    e. all of the above

    Answer: e

15. Changes in blood osmotic pressure would affect the levels of _____ in the blood.
    a. ACTH
    b. ADH
    c. oxytocin
    d. TSH
    e. gonadotropins

    Answer: b

16. Hormones that control the function of the anterior pituitary gland are
    released from the
    a. thalamus
    b. medulla oblongata
    c. hypothalamus
    d. pineal body
    e. cerebral nuclei

    Answer: c

17. The hypothalamus controls the secretions of the anterior pituitary by
    way of
    a. direct neural stimulation
    b. direct mechanical control
    c. releasing and inhibiting hormones
    d. altering ion concentrations in the anterior pituitary
    e. gap junctions

    Answer: c

18. When blood glucose levels rise
    a. insulin is released
    b. glucagon is released
    c. peripheral cells take up less glucose
    d. protein synthesis decreases
    e. a and c

    Answer: a

19. When blood glucose levels fall
    a. insulin is released
    b. glucagon is released
    c. peripheral cells take up less glucose
    d. protein synthesis decreases
    e. all of the above

    Answer: b

20. The enzyme renin is responsible for the activation of
    a. angiotensin
    b. cortisol
    c. erythropoietin
    d. ADH
    e. epinephrine

    Answer: a

21. The C cells of the thyroid gland produce
    a. thyroid hormone
    b. TSH
    c. calcitonin
    d. parathyroid hormone
    e. all of the above

    Answer: c

22. Parathyroid glands produce a hormone that
    a. stimulates the formation of white blood cells
    b. increases the level of calcium ions in the blood
    c. increases the level of sodium ions in the blood
    d. increases the level of potassium ions in the blood
    e. increases the level of glucose in the blood

    Answer: b

23. Cells of the adrenal cortex produce
    a. epinephrine
    b. ADH
    c. aldosterone
    d. parathyroid hormone
    e. insulin

    Answer: c

24. The alpha cells of the pancreas produce
    a. insulin
    b. glucagon
    c. renin
    d. ADH
    e. parathyroid hormone

    Answer: b

25. The beta cells of the pancreas produce
    a. insulin
    b. glucagon
    c. renin
    d. ADH
    e. parathyroid hormone

    Answer: a

26. Hormone-producing cells of the testes produce
    a. estrogen
    b. progesterone
    c. testosterone
    d. inhibin
    e. both c and d

    Answer: e

27. Follicle cells in the ovary produce large quantities of _____ when stimulated by FSH.
    a. estrogen
    b. progesterone
    c. testosterone
    d. inhibin
    e. a and b

    Answer: a

28. The posterior pituitary gland secretes
    a. FSH
    b. TSH
    c. ACTH
    d. ADH
    e. MSH

    Answer: d

29. The adrenal medulla produces
    a. androgens
    b. glucocorticoids
    c. mineralocorticoids
    d. epinephrine
    e. steroids

    Answer: d

30. The _____ lies within the abdominopelvic cavity near the border between the stomach and the small intestine.
    a. thymus gland
    b. adrenal gland
    c. pancreas
    d. thyroid gland
    e. testis

    Answer: c

31. The hormone oxytocin
    a. promotes uterine contractions
    b. is responsible for milk production in the mammary glands
    c. regulates blood pressure
    d. governs the ovarian cycle
    e. a and b

    Answer: e

32. Thyroid hormone contains the mineral
    a. sodium
    b. potassium
    c. iron
    d. iodine
    e. zinc

    Answer: d

33. The pituitary hormone that triggers the release of thyroid hormone from
    the thyroid gland is
    a. TSH
    b. ACTH
    c. FSH
    d. LH
    e. MSH

    Answer: a

34. The pituitary hormone that controls the release of glucocorticoids from
    the adrenal cortex is
    a. TSH
    b. ACTH
    c. FSH
    d. LH
    e. MSH

    Answer: b

35. The pituitary hormone that promotes egg development in ovaries and sperm
    development in testes is
    a. TSH
    b. ACTH
    c. FSH
    d. LH
    e. GH

    Answer: c

36. The pituitary hormone that promotes the ovarian secretion of progesterone and the testicular secretion of testosterone is
    a. TSH
    b. ACTH
    c. FSH
    d. LH
    e. GH

    Answer: d

37. The pituitary hormone that stimulates milk production by the mammary glands is
    a. TSH
    b. ACTH
    c. FSH
    d. LH
    e. PRL

    Answer: e

38. The pituitary hormone that stimulates melanocytes to produce melanin is
    a. TSH
    b. ACTH
    c. MSH
    d. LH
    e. GH

    Answer: c

39. A hormone that can lower blood levels of calcium ions is
    a. parathyroid hormone
    b. thyroid hormone
    c. calcitonin
    d. glucagon
    e. oxytocin

    Answer: c

40. Increased levels of the hormone _____ will lead to increased levels of calcium ion in the blood.
    a. thymosin
    b. calcitonin
    c. parathyroid hormone
    d. aldosterone
    e. cortisol

    Answer: c

41. The hormone that is important for maintenance of the immune system is
    a. thymosin
    b. cortisol
    c. aldosterone
    d. thyroid hormone
    e. gonadotropin

Answer: a

42. A hormone that helps to regulate the sodium ion concentration of the blood is
    a. cortisol
    b. parathyroid hormone
    c. thymosin
    d. growth hormone
    e. aldosterone

Answer: e

43. Increased numbers of red blood cells would result from increases in the hormone
    a. cortisol
    b. erythropoietin
    c. thymosin
    d. aldosterone
    e. renin

Answer: b

44. The pancreatic hormone that causes blood sugar levels to rise is
    a. growth hormone
    b. cortisol
    c. insulin
    d. glucagon
    e. erythropoietin

Answer: d

45. The pancreatic hormone that causes blood sugar levels to fall is
    a. cortisol
    b. growth hormone
    c. insulin
    d. glucagon
    e. aldosterone

Answer: c

46. The hormone that is the antagonist of calcitonin is
    a. insulin
    b. glucagon
    c. growth hormone
    d. parathyroid hormone
    e. thyroid hormone

    Answer: d

47. Hormones from which of the following is responsible for the calorigenic effect?
    a. pituitary gland
    b. adrenal gland
    c. parathyroid gland
    d. thyroid gland
    e. thymus

    Answer: d

48. Proper growth requires
    a. thyroid hormone
    b. insulin
    c. parathyroid hormone
    d. a and c only
    e. all of the above

    Answer: e

49. The hormone that dominates during the alarm phase of the general adaptation syndrome (GAS) is
    a. testosterone
    b. aldosterone
    c. cortisol
    d. thyroid hormone
    e. epinephrine

    Answer: e

50. During the alarm phase of the general adaptation syndrome (GAS) there is
    a. decreased blood flow to skeletal muscles and skin
    b. decreased mental alertness
    c. mobilization of energy reserves
    d. increased urine production
    e. all of the above

    Answer: c

51. If stress lasts longer than a few hours, an individual will enter which phase of the adaptation syndrome (GAS)?
    a. alarm phase
    b. resistance phase
    c. exhaustion phase
    d. extension phase
    e. prolonged phase

    Answer: b

52. The hormones that dominate during the resistance phase of the general adaptation syndrome (GAS) are the
    a. mineralocorticoids
    b. androgens
    c. glucocorticoids
    d. thyroid hormones
    e. gonadotropins

    Answer: c

53. The exhaustion phase of the general adaptation syndrome (GAS) is characterized by
    a. decreased resistance to disease and infection
    b. increased ability to produce glucose from glycogen
    c. increased pumping effectiveness of the heart
    d. increased protein synthesis
    e. a and c

    Answer: a

54. Excess secretion of growth hormone prior to puberty will cause
    a. dwarfism
    b. cancer
    c. gigantism
    d. acromegaly
    e. diabetes

    Answer: c

55. The condition known as cretinism is due to
    a. too much parathyroid hormone
    b. too little parathyroid hormone
    c. too much thyroid hormone
    d. too little thyroid hormone
    e. none of the above

    Answer: d

56. Inability of the pancreas to produce insulin would result in
    a. acromegaly
    b. myxedema
    c. diabetes mellitus
    d. diabetes insipidus
    e. Cushing's disease

    Answer: c

57. Hyposecretion of glucocorticoids would result in
    a. myxedema
    b. diabetes mellitus
    c. diabetes insipidus
    d. Addison's disease
    e. Cushing's disease

    Answer: d

58. Increased aggressive behavior is associated with increases in
    a. growth hormone
    b. thyroid hormone
    c. testosterone
    d. mineralocorticoids
    e. progesterone

    Answer: c

59. Which of the following is true concerning the interaction of the
    endocrine system with other body systems?
    a. Epinephrine stimulates respiratory activity and dilates respiratory
       passageways.
    b. Certain hormones control water and mineral balance by the kidneys.
    c. The heart secretes atrial natriuretic protein.
    d. b and c only
    e. all of the above

    Answer: e

60. In studying a group of cells, it is noticed that when stimulated by a
    particular hormone there is marked increase in the quantity of adenylate
    cyclase in a cell. The hormone being studied is probably
    a. a steroid
    b. a peptide
    c. testosterone
    d. estrogen
    e. aldosterone

    Answer: b

61. Diabetes insipidus is caused by
    a. decreased levels of insulin
    b. decreased numbers of insulin receptors
    c. decreased levels of ADH
    d. decreased numbers of ADH receptors
    e. none of the above

    Answer: c

62. Increased blood calcium levels would result in
    a. increased secretion of calcitonin
    b. increased secretion of parathyroid hormone
    c. increased retention of calcium by the kidneys
    d. increased osteoclast activity
    e. increased excitability of neural membranes

    Answer: a

63. Decreased levels of parathyroid hormone could result in
    a. tetany
    b. profuse urination
    c. increased sweating
    d. depressed immune activity
    e. all of the above

    Answer: a

64. Decreased blood flow to the kidneys would lead to
    a. renin release
    b. elevated levels of aldosterone
    c. increased levels of erythropoietin
    d. decreased levels of atrial natriuretic peptide
    e. all of the above

    Answer: e

65. In Type II diabetes, insulin levels are frequently normal, yet the target cells are less sensitive to the effects of insulin. This suggests that
    a. the target cells are impermeable to insulin
    b. the target cells may lack enough insulin receptors
    c. the target cells cannot convert insulin to an active form
    d. the target cells have adequate internal supplies of glucose
    e. none of the above

    Answer: b

66. The condition known as seasonal affective disorder (SAD) may be caused by
    a. exposure to too much sunlight
    b. increased levels of melatonin
    c. increased levels of MSH
    d. increased levels of gonadotrophins
    e. inability to produce sufficient amounts of melanin

Answer: b

67. Marissa has her thyroid gland removed because of a malignant tumor. She takes synthetic thyroid hormone to replace the thyroxine that her thyroid gland would have produced, but she is worried about her blood calcium since she has lost her source of calcitonin. Does she need to worry about this problem?
    a. No, the synthetic thyroid hormone will also control the calcium.
    b. No, as long as she still has functional parathyroid glands she will maintain proper levels of calcium.
    c. No, hormones from the liver and kidneys will regulate calcium through the intestinal tract.
    d. Yes, without the calcitonin, high blood levels of calcium will cause convulsions.
    e. Yes, without the calcitonin she will suffer heart failure.

Answer: b

68. Excessive urine production is known as
    a. polyphagia
    b. polydipsia
    c. polyuria
    d. polymyositis
    e. none of the above

Answer: c

69. This condition develops when the posterior pituitary no longer releases adequate amounts of ADH.
    a. diabetes mellitus
    b. diabetes insipidus
    c. pituitary dwarfism
    d. exophthalmos
    e. gigantism

Answer: b

70. This condition is characterized by abnormally high glucose
    concentrations that overwhelm the reabsorption capabilities of the
    kidneys.
    a. diabetes mellitus
    b. diabetes insipidus
    c. glucose diabetes
    d. gigantism
    e. all of the above

    Answer: a

71. Insulin-dependent diabetes mellitus is also known as
    a. non-insulin-dependent diabetes
    b. Type II
    c. Type III
    d. Type I
    e. diabetes insipidus

    Answer: d

72. Two hormones secreted by the posterior pituitary are:
    a. GH and TSH
    b. ACTH and LH
    c. ADH and FSH
    d. PRL and OT
    e. ADH and OT

    Answer: e

73. Two hormones secreted by the adrenal medulla are:
    a. CT and PTH
    b. epinephrine and norepinephrine
    c. PRL and ACTH
    d. oxytocin and ADH
    e. FSH and GH

    Answer: b

74. Effects of medullary hormones include all of the following **except**:
    a. increased heart activity
    b. increased blood pressure
    c. decreased glycogen breakdown
    d. release of lipids by adipose tissue
    e. increased blood glucose levels

    Answer: c

75. Another name for the pituitary gland is the
    a. infundibulum
    b. hypophyseal portal system
    c. hypothalamus
    d. hypophysis
    e. thymus

    Answer: d

76. This gland is responsible for establishing daily circadian rhythms.
    a. pineal
    b. pancreas
    c. thymus
    d. thyroid
    e. parathyroid

    Answer: a

Matching

77. Match the endocrine gland in the first column with its associated hormone in the second column.

    _____1. pituitary   A. cortisol
    _____2. thymus   B. melatonin
    _____3. thyroid   C. calcitonin
    _____4. pineal   D. growth hormone
    _____5. adrenal   E. thymosins

    Answer: 1-d, 2-e, 3-c, 4-b, 5-a

Fill-In-The-Blank

78. Peripheral cells sensitive to the presence of hormones are called _____ _____.

    Answer: target cells

79. Hormones that regulate the male and female reproductive organs are collectively called _____.

    Answer: gonadotropins

80. The thyroid gland is composed of many _____ that produce and store thyroid hormone.

    Answer: follicles

81. Thyroid hormones are structural derivatives of the amino acid _____.

    Answer: tyrosine

82. The _____ gland is located along the superior border of the kidney.

    Answer: adrenal

83. The outer layer of the adrenal gland is the adrenal _____.

    Answer: cortex

84. The inner portion of the adrenal gland is the adrenal _____.

    Answer: medulla

85. Two hormones that have opposing effects are called _____.

    Answer: antagonists

86. Two hormones that have additive effects are called _____.

    Answer: synergists

87. Any threat to homeostasis represents a form of _____.

    Answer: stress

88. The basic pattern of response that the body produces in response to stress is called the _____ _____ _____.

    Answer: general adaptation syndrome

Essay

89. Explain the interactions of the pancreatic hormones insulin and glucagon.

    Answer:
    Pancreatic islets contain alpha cells which produce the hormone glucagon, while the beta cells secrete insulin. Glucagon stimulates the conversion of glycogen to glucose, thus causing an increase in blood glucose concentration. Insulin serves to decrease the circulating level of blood glucose by promoting the transport of glucose into cells.

Chapter 12:   Blood

Multiple Choice

1. Functions of the blood include
   a. transport of nutrients and wastes
   b. regulation of pH and electrolyte concentration of interstitial fluids
   c. restricting fluid loss
   d. body defense
   e. all of the above

   Answer: e

2. Blood is composed of
   a. plasma
   b. formed elements
   c. blood cells
   d. cell fragments
   e. all of the above

   Answer: e

3. The formed elements of the blood include
   a. red blood cells
   b. clotting proteins
   c. defense proteins
   d. plasma proteins
   e. all of the above

   Answer: a

4. The combination of plasma and formed elements is called
   a. serum
   b. lymphatic fluid
   c. whole blood
   d. extracellular fluid
   e. packed blood

   Answer: c

5. Fresh whole blood is usually collected from
   a. the heart
   b. a superficial artery
   c. a superficial vein
   d. a capillary
   e. an arteriole

   Answer: c

6. Serum
   a. is the same as blood plasma
   b. is plasma minus the formed elements
   c. is plasma minus the proteins
   d. is plasma minus the clotting proteins
   e. is plasma minus the electrolytes

Answer: d

7. The chief difference between plasma and interstitial fluid involves
   a. the amount of water
   b. the quantity of electrolytes
   c. the quantity of organic wastes
   d. the concentration of dissolved gases and proteins
   e. the concentration of glucose

Answer: d

8. The most abundant proteins in blood plasma are
   a. globulins
   b. transport proteins
   c. albumins
   d. collagen
   e. fibrinogens

Answer: c

9. Plasma proteins that are important in body defense are
   a. albumins
   b. fibrinogens
   c. globulins
   d. collagens
   e. elastins

Answer: c

10. Plasma proteins that are necessary for blood clotting are the
    a. albumins
    b. fibrinogens
    c. globulins
    d. collagens
    e. elastins

Answer: b

11. Red blood cells are formed in
    a. the liver
    b. the spleen
    c. red bone marrow
    d. yellow bone marrow
    e. lymph nodes

Answer: c

12. About ____% of red blood cells are replaced every day.
    a. 1
    b. 2
    c. 3
    d. 5
    e. 8

Answer: a

13. Stem cells responsible for the production of white blood cells originate
    in the
    a. liver
    b. thymus
    c. spleen
    d. bone marrow
    e. lymph tissue

Answer: d

14. Red blood cell production is regulated by the hormone
    a. thymosin
    b. angiotensin
    c. erythropoietin
    d. ACTH
    e. LH

Answer: c

15. Phagocytosis of RBCs by macrophages occurs in
    a. the spleen
    b. bone marrow
    c. liver
    d. A and B
    e. all of these

Answer: e

16. Each of the following statements concerning red blood cells
    (erythrocytes) is true **except** one. Identify the exception.
    a. Red blood cells are biconcave discs.
    b. Red blood cells lack mitochondria.
    c. Red blood cells have a large nucleus.
    d. Red blood cells are specialized for carrying oxygen.
    e. Red blood cells contain hemoglobin.

    Answer: c

17. The average lifespan of a red blood cell is
    a. 1 week
    b. 1 month
    c. 4 months
    d. 6 months
    e. 1 year

    Answer: c

18. The function of red blood cells is
    a. to remove carbon dioxide from active cells
    b. to remove nitrogenous wastes from active tissues
    c. to carry oxygen from the lungs to the body's cells
    d. to carry nutrients from the digestive system to the body's cells
    e. to defend the body against infectious organisms

    Answer: c

19. The function of hemoglobin is to
    a. carry oxygen
    b. protect the body against infectious agents
    c. aid in the process of blood clotting
    d. carry nutrients from the intestine to the body's cells
    e. all of the above

    Answer: a

20. _____ is a condition in which the oxygen-carrying capacity of the
    blood is reduced.
    a. Erythropoiesis
    b. Lymphopoiesis
    c. Anemia
    d. Leukopenia
    e. Leukemia

    Answer: c

21. Aged and damaged erythrocytes are broken down by the
    a. spleen
    b. yellow bone marrow
    c. kidneys
    d. digestive tract
    e. thymus gland

    Answer: a

22. A hemoglobin molecule is composed of
    a. three protein chains and four heme groups
    b. two protein chains and two heme groups
    c. four protein chains and two heme groups
    d. four protein chains and four heme groups
    e. four protein chains and six heme groups

    Answer: d

23. Each heme group in a molecule of hemoglobin contains _____ atom(s) of iron.
    a. 1
    b. 2
    c. 3
    d. 4
    e. 1/2

    Answer: a

24. Most of the iron that is removed from degraded hemoglobin is
    a. excreted by the kidneys
    b. excreted by the liver
    c. excreted by the intestines
    d. recycled to the bone marrow
    e. stored in yellow bone marrow

    Answer: d

25. In adults, erythropoiesis primarily takes place in
    a. the liver
    b. yellow bone marrow
    c. myeloid tissue
    d. the spleen
    e. the kidneys

    Answer: c

26. Red bone marrow is located in the
    a. sternum
    b. ribs
    c. body of vertebrae
    d. ends of long bones
    e. all of the above

    Answer: e

27. The process of red blood cell production is called
    a. erythrocytosis
    b. erythropenia
    c. hemocytosis
    d. erythropoiesis
    e. hematopenia

    Answer: d

28. Erythropoiesis increases when
    a. oxygen levels in the blood increase
    b. oxygen levels in the blood decrease
    c. carbon dioxide levels in the blood increase
    d. carbon dioxide levels in the blood decrease
    e. protein levels in the blood increase

    Answer: b

29. A person's blood type is determined by
    a. the size of the red blood cells
    b. the shape of the red blood cells
    c. the chemical character of the hemoglobin
    d. the presence or absence of specific molecules on the cell membrane
    e. the number of specific molecules on the cell membrane

    Answer: d

30. A person with type A blood has
    a. A agglutinins on their red blood cells
    b. A agglutinogens in their plasma
    c. B agglutinogens on their red blood cells
    d. B agglutinins in their plasma
    e. the ability to receive AB blood cells

    Answer: d

31. Neutrophils
   a. are granular leukocytes
   b. are phagocytic
   c. have lobed nuclei
   d. are active in fighting bacterial infection
   e. all of the above

Answer: e

32. The most numerous white blood cells in peripheral circulation are the
   a. neutrophils
   b. eosinophils
   c. basophils
   d. lymphocytes
   e. monocytes

Answer: a

33. White blood cells that release histamine at the site of an injury are
   a. neutrophils
   b. eosinophils
   c. basophils
   d. lymphocytes
   e. monocytes

Answer: c

34. _____ are large phagocytic WBCs that are "transformed" into phagocytic macrophages at the site of an injury.
   a. Neutrophils
   b. Eosinophils
   c. Basophils
   d. Lymphocytes
   e. Monocytes

Answer: e

35. The white blood cells that are important in producing antibodies are the
   a. neutrophils
   b. eosinophils
   c. basophils
   d. lymphocytes
   e. monocytes

Answer: d

36. White blood cells that increase in number during an allergic reaction or in response to parasitic infections are the
    a. neutrophils
    b. eosinophils
    c. basophils
    d. lymphocytes
    e. monocytes

    Answer: b

37. Platelets function in
    a. transporting chemicals important for clotting
    b. forming temporary patches in injured areas
    c. contraction after clot formation
    d. initiating the clotting process
    e. all of the above

    Answer: e

38. Platelets are formed from cells in the bone marrow called
    a. erythroblasts
    b. normoblasts
    c. megakaryocytes
    d. reticulocytes
    e. lymphoblasts

    Answer: c

39. Platelets are
    a. large cells that lack a nucleus
    b. small cells that lack a nucleus
    c. large cells with a large nucleus
    d. small cells with a lobed nucleus
    e. fragments of large cells

    Answer: e

40. The following is a list of the steps involved in the process of hemostasis and clot removal.
    1. coagulation
    2. fibrinolysis
    3. vascular spasm
    4. retraction
    5. platelet phase

    The correct sequence of these steps is:
    a. 5, 1, 4, 2, 3
    b. 3, 5, 1, 4, 2
    c. 2, 3, 5, 1, 4
    d. 3, 4, 5, 2, 1
    e. 4, 3, 5, 2, 1

    Answer: b

41. The main event of the platelet phase is
    a. vascular spasm
    b. the activation of fibrinogen
    c. clot retraction
    d. the formation of a platelet plug
    e. the contraction of platelets

    Answer: d

42. _____ involves a complex sequence of steps leading to the conversion of fibrinogen to fibrin.
    a. Vascular spasm
    b. The platelet phase
    c. Retraction
    d. Coagulation
    e. Fibrinolysis

    Answer: d

43. The extrinsic pathway of coagulation is activated by
    a. the sticking of platelets to damaged tissue
    b. the activation of a proenzyme exposed to collagen
    c. the release of tissue factor by damaged endothelium
    d. the release of heparin from the liver
    e. the conversion of prothrombin to thrombin

    Answer: c

44. The common pathway of coagulation begins with
    a. the sticking of platelets to damaged tissue
    b. the activation of a proenzyme exposed to collagen
    c. the release of tissue factor by damaged endothelium
    d. the activating of a clotting factor that converts prothrombin to thrombin
    e. the activation of a clotting factor that converts fibrinogen to fibrin

    Answer: d

45. The process of fibrinolysis
    a. activates fibrinogen
    b. draws torn edges of damaged tissue closer together
    c. dissolves clots
    d. forms emboli
    e. forms thrombi

    Answer: c

46. Which of the following vitamins is needed for the formation of clotting factors?
    a. vitamin A
    b. vitamin B
    c. vitamin C
    d. vitamin K
    e. vitamin E

    Answer: d

47. A drifting blood clot is called a(n)
    a. embolus
    b. thrombus
    c. plaque
    d. coagulant
    e. platelet plug

    Answer: a

48. With respect to the Rh factor, which of the following statements is true?
    a. Rh agglutinogens are not found on the surface of the red blood cells.
    b. Rh agglutinogens do not produce a cross reaction.
    c. Individuals who are Rh- do not carry agglutinins to Rh factor unless they have been previously sensitized.
    d. Rh agglutinogens are found free in the plasma.
    e. all of the above

    Answer: c

49. During a viral infection you would expect to see increased numbers of
    a. neutrophils
    b. eosinophils
    c. basophils
    d. lymphocytes
    e. thrombocytes

Answer: d

50. A sample of tissue from an injury shows a large number of basophils. This would indicate that the tissue was
    a. abscessed
    b. inflamed
    c. being rejected
    d. infected by viruses
    e. infected by parasites

Answer: b

51. Rat poison contains a toxin that blocks the liver's ability to utilize vitamin K. Animals that consume rat poison would die of
    a. asphyxiation
    b. acidosis
    c. hemorrhage
    d. leukemia
    e. anemia

Answer: c

52. How would a decrease in the concentration of calcium ion in the blood affect the process of hemostasis?
    a. platelet plugs would fail to form
    b. coagulation would proceed more rapidly
    c. coagulation would proceed more slowly
    d. retraction would occur prematurely
    e. fibrinolysis would occur more quickly

Answer: c

53. A person who lives in a city at sea level and vacations in the Rocky Mountains would experience an increase in:
    a. the number of platelets in their blood
    b. the number of lymphocytes in their blood
    c. his/her red blood cell count
    d. his/her white blood cell count
    e. the density of their bone marrow

Answer: c

54. A constriction of the arteries that carry blood to the kidneys would result in
    a. anemia
    b. increased numbers of lymphocytes
    c. increased erythropoiesis
    d. decreased erythropoiesis
    e. decreased elimination of vitamin K

Answer: c

55. What affect would a drug that interferes with protein synthesis have on the development of red blood cells?
    a. Fewer cells than normal would be formed.
    b. The cells formed would not be able to carry as much oxygen as normal.
    c. The cells formed would carry larger amounts of carbon dioxide.
    d. The cells would be round like spheres.
    e. all of the above

Answer: b

56. Bill wants to determine his blood type, so he takes a few drops of blood from a puncture wound in his finger and mixes it with various antisera. His blood cells agglutinate when mixed with the anti-A sera but not with the anti-B or anti-Rh sera. This means
    a. Bill could receive type B blood in a transfusion
    b. Bill could donate blood to an individual with type AB blood
    c. Bill is Rh-positive
    d. Bill's plasma contains B agglutinins
    e. Bill's plasma would cross-react with type 0 negative red blood cells

Answer: d

57. This disease is characterized by an inability to produce adequate amounts of two of the four globular protein components of hemoglobin.
    a. sickle cell anemia
    b. thalassemia
    c. hematuria
    d. jaundice
    e. aplastic anemia

Answer: b

58. This condition results from a mutation affecting the amino acid sequence of one of the globular proteins of the hemoglobin molecule.
    a. hematuria
    b. aplastic anemia
    c. microcytic anemia
    d. jaundice
    e. sickle cell anemia

Answer: e

59. Another term for the condition known as erythroblastosis fetalis is
    a. sensitization incompatibility
    b. cross reaction
    c. hemolytic disease of the newborn
    d. anemia
    e. none of the above

    Answer: c

60. Calcium ions and _____ have an effect on nearly every aspect of the clotting process.
    a. vitamin K
    b. vitamin A
    c. vitamin D
    d. vitamin E
    e. thiamin

    Answer: a

61. _____ occur(s) where endothelial and smooth muscle cells contain large quantities of lipids.
    a. Clots
    b. Emboli
    c. Coagulation
    d. Plaques
    e. Stasis

    Answer: d

62. The inherited condition resulting from the inadequate production of clotting factors is termed _____.
    a. anemia
    b. thalassemia
    c. jaundice
    d. hemophilia
    e. none of the above

    Answer: d

63. Which of the following represents the correct sequence of appearance for mature red blood cells?
    a. stem cell, erythroblast stage, proerythroblast, reticulocyte, RBC
    b. hemocytoblast, myeloblast, reticulocyte, megakaryocyte, RBC
    c. myeloid stem cell, proerythroblast, erythroblast, reticulocyte, RBC
    d. monoblast, promonocyte, myelocyte, band cell, RBC
    e. lymphoblast, proerythroblast, reticulocyte, band cell, RBC

    Answer: c

64. All of the following conditions may result in an <u>increased</u> white blood cell count **except**:
    a. acute infections
    b. leukemia
    c. menstruation
    d. aplastic anemia
    e. all of the above

    Answer: d

65. All of the following conditions may result in an <u>increased</u> red blood cell count.
    a. severe dehydration, diarrhea, polycythemia
    b. anemia, dehydration, leukemia
    c. anemia, dehydration, severe hemorrhage
    d. leukemia, anemia, and severe dehydration
    e. anemia, polycythemia, and dehydration

    Answer: a

Matching

66. Match the plasma protein in the first column with its characteristic in the second.

    _____1. albumins   A. major contributors to maintaining osmotic
    _____2. globulins   pressure
    _____3. fibrinogen   B. functions in the clotting reaction
                           C. involved in immunity

    Answer: 1-a, 2-c, 3-b

Fill-In-The-Blank

67. The percentage of whole blood occupied by cellular elements is termed the _____.

    Answer: hematocrit

68. Blood is approximately ____% plasma by volume.

    Answer: 55

69. Hormones called _____ _____ _____ are involved in regulation of WBC populations.

    Answer: colony-stimulating factors

70. Erythropoiesis is closely regulated by a circulating hormone called _____ _____ .

    Answer: erythropoiesis-stimulating hormone or erythropoietin or EPO

71. The _____ _____ is a procedure that is used to determine the number of each of the various types of white blood cells.

    Answer: differential count

72. A fibrin network that contains trapped blood cells and platelets is called a(n) _____ _____ .

    Answer: blood clot

Essay

73. In the disease mononucleosis ("mono"), the spleen enlarges because of increased numbers of cells--both phagocytic as well as others. Common symptoms of this disease include pale complexion, a tired feeling, and a lack of energy sometimes to the point of not being able to get out of bed. What might cause these symptoms?

    Answer:
    A major function of the spleen is to destroy old, defective, and worn out red blood cells. As the spleen increases in size, so does its capacity to eliminate red blood cells and this produces anemia. The decreased number of red blood cells decreases the blood's ability to deliver oxygen to the tissues and thus their metabolism is slowed down. This would account for the tired feeling and lack of energy. Because there are fewer red blood cells than normal, the blood circulating through the skin is not as red and so the person has a pale or white skin coloration.

Chapter 13: The Heart

Multiple Choice

1. The heart lies in the
   a. pleural cavity
   b. peritoneal cavity
   c. abdominopelvic cavity
   d. mediastinum
   e. none of the above

   Answer: d

2. The expandable extension of the atrium is the
   a. ventricle
   b. coronary sinus
   c. coronary sulcus
   d. auricle
   e. interatrial septum

   Answer: d

3. The portion of the pericardial membrane that lies directly on the surface of the heart is the
   a. visceral pericardium
   b. parietal pericardium
   c. visceral endocardium
   d. parietal myocardium
   e. parietal endocardium

   Answer: a

4. The visceral pericardium is the same as the
   a. mediastinum
   b. parietal pericardium
   c. epicardium
   d. myocardium
   e. endocardium

   Answer: c

5. The functions of the pericardium include which of the following?
   a. returning blood to the atria
   b. pumping blood into circulation
   c. removing excess fluid from the heart chambers
   d. anchoring the heart to surrounding structures
   e. preventing expansion of the heart

   Answer: d

6. Blood returning from the systemic circuit first enters the
   a. right atrium
   b. right ventricle
   c. left atrium
   d. left ventricle
   e. none of the above

   Answer: a

7. Blood returning from the lungs enters the
   a. right atrium
   b. right ventricle
   c. left atrium
   d. left ventricle
   e. none of the above

   Answer: c

8. The right ventricle pumps blood
   a. to the lungs
   b. to the left ventricle
   c. to the left atrium
   d. to the systemic circuit
   e. none of the above

   Answer: a

9. The left ventricle pumps blood
   a. to the lungs
   b. to the right ventricle
   c. to the right atrium
   d. to the systemic circuit
   e. none of the above

   Answer: d

10. The right atrium receives blood from the
    a. pulmonary veins
    b. pulmonary trunk
    c. aorta
    d. inferior vena cava
    e. none of the above

    Answer: d

11. The atrioventricular valve that is located on the side of the heart that receives the superior vena cava is the
    a. mitral valve
    b. bicuspid valve
    c. tricuspid valve
    d. pulmonary semilunar valve
    e. aortic semilunar valve

Answer: c

12. Blood leaving the right ventricle enters the
    a. pulmonary veins
    b. pulmonary trunk
    c. aorta
    d. inferior vena cava
    e. superior vena cava

Answer: b

13. The pulmonary semilunar valve guards the entrance to the
    a. aorta
    b. pulmonary trunk
    c. pulmonary veins
    d. right ventricle
    e. left ventricle

Answer: b

14. The bicuspid or mitral valve is located
    a. in the opening of the aorta
    b. in the opening of the pulmonary trunk
    c. where the vena cavae join the right atrium
    d. between the right atrium and right ventricle
    e. between the left atrium and left ventricle

Answer: e

15. The entrance to the ascending aorta is guarded by
    a. an atrioventricular valve
    b. a semilunar valve
    c. the bicuspid valve
    d. the tricuspid valve
    e. the mitral valve

Answer: b

16. The function of an atrium is
    a. to collect blood
    b. to pump blood to the lungs
    c. to pump blood into the systemic circuit
    d. to pump blood to the heart muscle
    e. all of the above

    Answer: a

17. The following is a list of vessels and structures that are associated
    with the heart.
    1. right atrium
    2. left atrium
    3. right ventricle
    4. left ventricle
    5. vena cavae
    6. aorta
    7. pulmonary trunk
    8. pulmonary veins

    What is the correct order for the flow of blood entering from the
    systemic circulation?
    a. 1,2,7,8,3,4,6,5
    b. 1,7,3,8,2,4,6,5
    c. 5,1,3,7,8,2,4,6
    d. 5,3,1,7,8,4,2,6
    e. 5,1,3,8,7,2,4,6

    Answer: c

18. The left and right pulmonary arteries carry blood to the
    a. heart
    b. lungs
    c. brain
    d. intestines
    e. liver

    Answer: b

19. The left and right pulmonary veins carry blood to the
    a. heart
    b. lungs
    c. brain
    d. intestines
    e. liver

    Answer: a

20. The heart wall is composed of _____ layers of tissue.
    a. 2
    b. 3
    c. 4
    d. 5
    e. 6

Answer: b

21. The myocardium is primarily composed of
    a. elastic tissue
    b. fibrous connective tissue
    c. epithelial tissue
    d. cardiac muscle tissue
    e. smooth muscle tissue

Answer: d

22. The fibrous skeleton of the heart functions to
    a. physically isolate the muscle fibers of the atria from those of the ventricles
    b. maintain the normal shape of the heart
    c. help distribute the forces of cardiac contraction
    d. a and c only
    e. all of the above

Answer: e

23. The first blood vessels to branch from the aorta are the
    a. pulmonary arteries
    b. coronary arteries
    c. circumflex arteries
    d. carotid arteries
    e. subclavian arteries

Answer: b

24. The marginal branch and posterior interventricular branch are branches of the
    a. right coronary artery
    b. left coronary artery
    c. circumflex artery
    d. coronary sinus
    e. aorta

Answer: a

25. The circumflex branch and the anterior descending artery are branches of the
    a. right coronary artery
    b. left coronary artery
    c. interventricular artery
    d. coronary sinus
    e. aorta

    Answer: b

26. The great and middle cardiac veins drain blood into the
    a. superior vena cava
    b. inferior vena cava
    c. coronary sinus
    d. coronary sulcus
    e. aorta

    Answer: c

27. The action potential in a cardiac muscle fiber lasts about ____ times longer than the action potential in a skeletal muscle fiber.
    a. 5
    b. 15
    c. 30
    d. 45
    e. 60

    Answer: c

28. The maximum rate of contraction in normal cardiac muscle fibers is _____ per minute.
    a. 80
    b. 140
    c. 200
    d. 250
    e. 300+

    Answer: c

29. Which of the following is true regarding cardiac muscle?
    a. neither summation nor tetany can occur
    b. both summation and tetany can occur
    c. summation, but not tetany, can occur
    d. tetany, but not summation, can occur
    e. none of the above are true

    Answer: a

30. The heart is innervated by
    a. parasympathetic nerves
    b. sympathetic nerves
    c. both parasympathetic and sympathetic nerves

    Answer: c

31. The pacemaker cells of the heart are located in the
    a. Purkinje fibers
    b. SA node
    c. AV node
    d. wall of the left ventricle
    e. both the left and right ventricles

    Answer: b

32. The following are various components of the conducting system of the heart.
    1. Purkinje cells
    2. AV bundle
    3. AV node
    4. SA node
    5. bundle branches

    The sequence in which an action potential would move through this system is
    a. 1, 4, 3, 2, 5
    b. 3, 2, 4, 5, 1
    c. 3, 5, 4, 2, 1
    d. 4, 3, 2, 5, 1
    e. 4, 2, 3, 5, 1

    Answer: d

33. Spontaneous depolarization of the nodal tissue in the SA node occurs at ____ action potential per minute.
    a. 30
    b. 50
    c. 70-80
    d. 100-120
    e. 150

    Answer: c

34. Depolarization of the ventricles is represented on an electrocardiogram by the
    a. p wave
    b. t wave
    c. s wave
    d. QRS complex
    e. PR complex

    Answer: d

35. The T wave on an ECG tracing represents
    a. atrial depolarization
    b. atrial repolarization
    c. ventricular depolarization
    d. ventricular repolarization
    e. ventricular contraction

    Answer: d

36. The first heart sound is heard when
    a. the AV valves open
    b. the AV valves close
    c. the semilunar valves close
    d. the atria contract
    e. blood enters the aorta

    Answer: b

37. Relaxation of the ventricles is called
    a. ventricular diastole
    b. ventricular systole

    Answer: a

38. The p wave of the ECG corresponds to
    a. atrial depolarization
    b. atrial diastole
    c. ventricular systole
    d. ventricular diastole
    e. none of the above

    Answer: a

39. The QRS complex of the ECG corresponds to
    a. atrial systole
    b. atrial diastole
    c. ventricular systole
    d. ventricular diastole
    e. none of the above

    Answer: c

40. The volume of blood ejected from each ventricle during a contraction is called the
    a. diastolic volume
    b. systolic volume
    c. stroke volume
    d. cardiac output
    e. cardiac reserve

    Answer: c

41. The cardiac output is equal to
    a. the difference between the diastolic volume and the systolic volume
    b. the product of heart rate and stroke volume
    c. the difference between the stroke volume at rest and the stroke volume during exercise
    d. the stroke volume less the systolic volume
    e. the product of heart rate and blood pressure

    Answer: b

42. Each of the following factors will increase cardiac output **except** one. Identify the exception.
    a. increased venous return
    b. increased parasympathetic stimulation
    c. increased sympathetic stimulation
    d. increased heart rate
    e. increased force of ventricular contraction

    Answer: b

43. According to Starling's law of the heart, the cardiac output is directly related to
    a. the size of the ventricle
    b. the heart rate
    c. the venous return
    d. the thickness of the myocardium
    e. the amount of blood in the circulatory system

    Answer: c

44. Cardiac muscle is similar to skeletal muscle in
    a. the arrangement of the t-tubules
    b. the arrangement of the sarcoplasmic reticulum
    c. the presence of striations
    d. the presence of intercalated discs
    e. all of the above

    Answer: c

45. At an intercalated disc
    a. the cell membranes of two cardiac muscle fibers are completely separated by a synapse
    b. the myofibrils are loosely attached to the membrane of the disc
    c. two cardiac muscle cells are connected by gap junctions
    d. t-tubules unite the membranes of the adjoining cells
    e. all of the above

    Answer: c

46. During ventricular systole
    a. the atria are contracting
    b. blood is entering the ventricles
    c. the AV valves are closed
    d. the pressure in the ventricles declines
    e. the ventricles are relaxed

    Answer: c

47. Which of the following is longer?
    a. the refractory period of cardiac muscle
    b. the refractory period of skeletal muscle

    Answer: a

48. As a result of the long refractory period, cardiac muscle cannot exhibit
    a. tone (tonus)
    b. relaxation
    c. tetany
    d. recruitment
    e. fatigue

    Answer: c

49. Which of the following is greater?
    a. the conduction velocity along a normal myocardial fiber
    b. the conduction velocity along a Purkinje fiber

    Answer: b

50. Which of the following is greater during left ventricular systole?
    a. the pressure in the ventricle
    b. the pressure in the aorta

    Answer: a

51. If the connections between the vagus nerve and the heart are severed
    a. the heart will beat slower
    b. the stroke volume will decrease
    c. the cardiac output will decrease
    d. the nodal fibers will depolarize more slowly
    e. none of the above

    Answer: e

52. Cardiac output would be greatest when
    a. sympathetic stimulation of the heart increases
    b. parasympathetic stimulation of the heart increases

    Answer: a

53. If the connection between the SA node and AV node becomes blocked,
    a. the ventricles will beat faster
    b. the ventricles will beat more slowly
    c. the ventricular rate of contraction will not be affected
    d. the stroke volume will increase
    e. tachycardia will occur

    Answer: b

54. If a myocardial infarction results in the formation of scar tissue along the pathway of the left bundle branch,
    a. cardiac arrhythmias may occur
    b. blood flow to the lungs will decrease
    c. the ventricle will contract more forcefully
    d. conduction through the left ventricle would remain normal
    e. the right ventricle will fail to contract

    Answer: a

55. In which situation would the stroke volume be the greatest?
    a. when venous return is increased
    b. when venous return is decreased
    c. when the force of contraction is decreased
    d. when the difference between the end diastolic volume and the end systolic volume is small
    e. when calcium channel blockers are present

    Answer: a

56. An inflammation of the heart tissue is referred to as
    a. myositis
    b. carditis
    c. prolapse
    d. stenosis
    e. infarction

    Answer: b

57. Rheumatic fever, which can lead to rheumatic heart disorder, is caused by _____ bacteria.
    a. pneumococcal
    b. streptococcal
    c. vibrio
    d. spirillum
    e. gonococcal

    Answer: b

58. In this condition, the bicuspid valves do not close properly.
    a. mitral valve prolapse
    b. semilunar valve prolapse
    c. ventricular stenosis
    d. atrioventricular valve prolapse
    e. overriding aorta

    Answer: a

59. Under conditions of hypercalcemia,
    a. cardiac muscle cells become lethargic
    b. cardiac muscle contraction is weak
    c. cardiac muscles become extremely excitable
    d. cardiac muscle cells remain the same
    e. none of the above

    Answer: c

60. Hypokalemia results in
    a. increased heart rate
    b. weak cardiac contractions
    c. reduced heart rate
    d. A and B
    e. none of the above

    Answer: c

61. Body temperature below normal results in all of the following **except**:
    a. higher rate of depolarization at the SA node
    b. slower rate of depolarization at the SA node
    c. lower heart rate
    d. reduced strength of cardiac contractions
    e. none of the above

    Answer: a

62. The _____ _____ accelerates the heart rate when the walls of the right atrium are stretched.
    a. venous return
    b. stroke volume
    c. cardiac output
    d. atrial reflex
    e. cardiac cycle

    Answer: d

63. The cardioacceleratory center in the medulla oblongata activates _____ neurons.
    a. sympathetic
    b. preganglionic
    c. postganglionic
    d. parasympathetic
    e. ganglionic

    Answer: a

64. The cardioinhibitory center controls activities of the _____ neurons.
    a. ganglionic
    b. parasympathetic
    c. postganglionic
    d. preganglionic
    e. sympathetic

    Answer: b

Matching

65. Match the structure in the first column with its description in the second column.

    _____1. systole   A. relaxation of heart chambers
    _____2. diastole   B. period of cardiac contraction
    _____3. anastomoses   C. pace-maker of heart
    _____4. SA node   D. amount of blood ejected by the left
    _____5. cardiac output   ventricle each minute
                               E. juncture of two peripheral vessels with the
                                  capillary bed

    Answer: 1a-b, 2-a, 3-e, 4-c, 5-d

Fill-In-The-Blank

66. The superior chambers of the heart are called _____ and the inferior chambers are the _____.

    Answer: atria; ventricles

67. The dense _____ _____ supports the heart's contractile cells and valves.

    Answer: fibrous skeleton

68. The heart is surrounded by the _____ cavity.

    Answer: pericardial

69. The fibrous sac that surrounds the heart and is continuous with the pericardium is the _____.

    Answer: pericardium

70. The left border of the heart is formed by the _____ _____ and a small portion of the _____ _____.

    Answer: left ventricle; left atrium

71. The wall of the _____ _____ forms most of the inferior border of the heart.

    Answer: right ventricle

72. The great vessels of the heart are located at the _____ of the heart.

    Answer: base

73. The _____ circuit carries blood to and from the lungs.

    Answer: pulmonary

74. The _____ circuit carries blood to and from all parts of the body except the lungs.

    Answer: systemic

75. _____ are blood vessels that carry blood away from the heart.

    Answer: Arteries

76. _____ are blood vessels that return blood to the heart.

    Answer: Veins

77. The _____ is the same as the visceral pericardium and covers the outer surface of the heart.

    Answer: epicardium

243

78. The muscle layer of the heart is the _____.

    Answer: myocardium

79. The _____ lines the chambers of the heart, the heart valves and is continuous with the lining of the attached blood vessels.

    Answer: endocardium

80. The property of heart muscle to contract in the absence of neural or hormonal stimulation is called _____.

    Answer: automaticity or autorhythmicity

81. The cells responsible for establishing the rate of a cardiac contraction are the _____ cells.

    Answer: nodal

82. A slower than normal heart rate is called _____.

    Answer: bradycardia

83. A faster than normal heart rate is called _____.

    Answer: tachycardia

84. The period between the start of one heartbeat and the beginning of the next is called the _____ _____.

    Answer: cardiac cycle

85. The contraction phase of the cardiac cycle is called _____.

    Answer: systole

86. The relaxation phase of the cardiac cycle is called _____.

    Answer: diastole

87. Abnormal patterns of cardiac activity are known as _____.

    Answer: arrhythmias

88. In a condition called _____ _____ _____ the cusps of the mitral valve do not close properly.

    Answer: mitral valve prolapse

89. In a condition called heart _____, the heart is unable to maintain an adequate cardiac output.

    Answer: failure

90. The amount of blood returning to the heart is the _____ _____.

    Answer: venous return

91. Atherosclerosis of coronary vessels leads to _____ _____ _____.

    Answer: coronary artery disease

92. The term for reduced blood flow to the cardiac muscle is _____ _____.

    Answer: coronary ischemia

93. A procedure in which a small section of a peripheral vein is used to create a detour around an obstruction in a coronary artery is called _____ _____ _____.

    Answer: coronary bypass surgery

Essay

94. Vern is brought into the emergency room of a hospital suffering from cardiac arrhythmias. In the emergency room he begins to exhibit tachycardia and as a result loses consciousness. His anxious wife asks you why he has lost consciousness. What would you tell her?

    Answer:
    During tachycardia, the heart beats at an abnormally fast rate. The faster the heart beats, the less time there is in between contractions for it to fill with blood again. As a result, over a period of time the heart fills with less and less blood and thus pumps less blood out. The stroke volume decreases, as does the cardiac output. When the cardiac output decreases to the point where not enough blood reaches the central nervous system, loss of consciousness occurs.

95. Explain the significance of the thickness of the left ventricular wall.

    Answer:
    The thicker wall of the left ventricle allows it to contract forcefully with great pressure to move the blood systemically. The wall of the right ventricle is thinner so that a lower pressure is created to move the blood a relatively short distance to the lungs.

Chapter 14: Blood Vessels and Circulation

Multiple Choice

1. The muscular layer of blood vessels is the
   a. tunica intima
   b. tunica externa
   c. tunica media
   d. tunica interna
   e. tunica adventitia

   Answer: c

2. Compared to arteries, veins
   a. are more elastic
   b. have more smooth muscle in their tunica media
   c. have a pleated endothelium
   d. have thinner walls
   e. hold their shape better when cut

   Answer: d

3. The following is a list of the vessels that blood passes through exiting the heart and then returning back to the heart.
   1. venules
   2. arterioles
   3. capillaries
   4. elastic arteries
   5. medium veins
   6. large veins
   7. muscular arteries

   The correct order in which blood passes through these structures after leaving the heart until its return is
   a. 7, 4, 2, 3, 1, 5, 6
   b. 6, 5, 1, 3, 2, 7, 4
   c. 5, 6, 1, 3, 2, 7, 4
   d. 2, 7, 6, 3, 1, 5, 6
   e. 4, 7, 2, 3, 1, 5, 6

   Answer: e

4. The blood vessels that play the most important role in the regulation of blood flow to a tissue and blood pressure are the
   a. arteries
   b. arterioles
   c. veins
   d. venules
   e. capillaries

   Answer: b

5. The only blood vessels whose walls permit exchange between the blood and the surrounding interstitial fluids are the
   a. arteries
   b. arterioles
   c. veins
   d. venules
   e. capillaries

   Answer: e

6. Blood flow through a capillary is regulated by the
   a. endothelium
   b. capillary bed itself
   c. precapillary sphincter
   d. heart action
   e. central channel

   Answer: c

7. Blood moves forward through veins
   a. because the pressure in the veins is lower than in the arteries
   b. with the aid of contractions of skeletal muscles
   c. with the aid of changes in cavity pressure
   d. a and b only
   e. all of the above

   Answer: e

8. Blood flow through the circulatory system is affected by
   a. pressure differences
   b. the viscosity of the blood
   c. the amount of friction in the blood vessels
   d. the length and diameter of the blood vessels
   e. all of the above

   Answer: e

9. Blood osmotic pressure is most affected by changes in
   a. the concentration of plasma sodium ions
   b. the concentration of plasma waste glucose
   c. the concentration of plasma waste products
   d. the concentration of plasma proteins
   e. the number of white blood cells

   Answer: d

10. Each of the following statements concerning the movement of fluid between capillaries and interstitial spaces is true **except** one. Identify the exception.
    a. Blood hydrostatic pressure forces fluid from the capillary into the interstitial space.
    b. Blood osmotic pressure moves fluid from the interstitial space into the capillary.
    c. The blood hydrostatic pressure and the blood osmotic pressure are equal in magnitude but opposite in direction.

    Answer: c

11. As blood travels from the aorta toward the capillaries
    a. the pressure increases
    b. the resistance increases
    c. the flow increases
    d. the viscosity increases
    e. all of the above

    Answer: b

12. Blood pressure is determined by
    a. measuring the size of the pulse
    b. measuring the pressure in the left ventricle
    c. measuring the force exerted by blood in a vessel against air in a closed cuff
    d. measuring the degree of turbulence in a closed vessel
    e. all of the above

    Answer: c

13. Blood pressure increases with
    a. increased cardiac output
    b. increased peripheral resistance
    c. increased blood volume
    d. b and c only
    e. all of the above

    Answer: e

14. The difference between the systolic and diastolic pressures is called the
    a. critical closing pressure
    b. mean arterial pressure
    c. pulse pressure
    d. blood pressure
    e. circulatory pressure

    Answer: c

15. The cycles of alternating contraction and relaxation seen in precapillary sphincters is called
    a. autoregulation
    b. ambulation
    c. vasomotion
    d. sphincterization
    e. contractual beating

Answer: c

16. Each of the following will cause an increase in blood pressure **except** one. Identify the exception.
    a. increased levels of aldosterone
    b. increased levels of angiotensin II
    c. increased blood volume
    d. increased levels of ANP (atrial natriuretic peptide)
    e. increased levels of ADH (antidiuretic hormone)

Answer: d

17. Each of the following changes will result in increased blood flow to a tissue **except** one. Identify the exception.
    a. increased blood volume
    b. increased vessel diameter
    c. increased blood pressure
    d. decreased peripheral resistance
    e. relaxation of precapillary sphincters

Answer: b

18. The goal of cardiovascular regulation is to
    a. ensure that blood flow changes occur at the appropriate time
    b. ensure that blood flow changes occur in the appropriate area
    c. ensure that changes occur without drastically altering blood pressure
    d. ensure that changes occur without drastically altering blood flow to a vital organ
    e. all of the above

Answer: e

19. Cardiovascular functions are regulated by all of the following factors **except** one. Choose the exception.
    a. neural factors
    b. venous return
    c. endocrine factors
    d. glucose concentration

Answer: d

20. Baroreceptors that function in the regulation of blood pressure are located in the
    a. left ventricle
    b. brain stem
    c. carotid sinus
    d. common iliac artery
    e. all of the above

    Answer: c

21. During increased exercise
    a. vasoconstriction occurs at the active skeletal muscles
    b. venous return increases
    c. cardiac output decreases
    d. stroke volume decreases
    e. all of the above

    Answer: b

22. In response to hemorrhage, there is
    a. decreased vasomotor tone
    b. increased parasympathetic stimulation of the heart
    c. mobilization of the venous reserve
    d. a and c only
    e. all of the above

    Answer: c

23. Symptoms of shock include
    a. hypotension
    b. rapid, weak pulse
    c. decreased urine formation
    d. acidosis
    e. all of the above

    Answer: e

24. Homeostatic mechanisms can compensate for circulatory shock during the
    a. ischemic stage
    b. progressive stage
    c. compensated stage
    d. reversible stage
    e. irreversible stage

    Answer: c

25. An important artery that supplies blood to the brain is
    a. external carotid
    b. subclavian
    c. vertebral
    d. brachiocephalic
    e. maxillary

    Answer: c

26. Blood from the brain returns to the heart by way of the
    a. vertebral vein
    b. axillary
    c. brachiocephalic
    d. internal jugular
    e. external jugular

    Answer: d

27. Branches off the aortic arch include
    a. the right subclavian artery
    b. the left subclavian artery
    c. the right common carotid artery
    d. the right axillary artery
    e. all of the above

    Answer: b

28. After passing the first rib, the subclavian artery becomes the
    a. radial artery
    b. ulnar artery
    c. brachial artery
    d. axillary artery
    e. digital artery

    Answer: d

29. In the upper arm, the axillary artery becomes the
    a. radial artery
    b. ulnar artery
    c. brachial artery
    d. subclavian artery
    e. carotid artery

    Answer: c

30. The brachial artery branches to form the
    a. radial and axillary arteries
    b. radial and digital arteries
    c. radial and ulnar arteries
    d. radial and subclavian arteries
    e. radial and brachiocephalic arteries

    Answer: c

31. The two vertebral arteries fuse to form a large artery, the
    a. circle of Willis
    b. common carotid
    c. external carotid
    d. internal carotid
    e. basilar

    Answer: e

32. The internal carotids and the basilar artery are interconnected by an anastomosis called the
    a. common carotid artery
    b. cerebral ring
    c. circle of Willis
    d. external carotid artery
    e. none of the above

    Answer: c

33. At the carotid sinus,
    a. the common carotid forms an internal and an external branch
    b. the internal carotids fuse with the vertebral arteries
    c. the external carotid forms the internal carotid
    d. veins and arteries anastomose
    e. the aorta gives rise to the common carotids

    Answer: a

34. The _____ divides the aorta into a superior thoracic aorta and an inferior abdominal aorta.
    a. pericardium
    b. mediastinum
    c. diaphragm
    d. peritoneum
    e. pleura

    Answer: c

35. Near the level of vertebra L4, the aorta branches to form the
    a. common carotid arteries
    b. common iliac arteries
    c. femoral arteries
    d. popliteal arteries
    e. tibial arteries

    Answer: b

36. The external iliac artery branches to form the
    a. radial and ulnar artery
    b. femoral and popliteal artery
    c. femoral and tibial artery
    d. tibial and popliteal artery
    e. femoral and deep femoral artery

    Answer: e

37. The vessel that receives blood from the head, neck, chest, shoulders, and arms is the
    a. internal jugular vein
    b. external jugular vein
    c. superior vena cava
    d. inferior vena cava
    e. coronary sinus

    Answer: c

38. Small veins of the brain empty into the
    a. coronary sinuses
    b. dural sinuses
    c. circle of Willis
    d. external jugular vein
    e. vertebral veins

    Answer: b

39. The dural sinuses collect blood from the
    a. heart
    b. lungs
    c. brain
    d. arms
    e. legs

    Answer: c

40. The radial and ulnar veins fuse to form the
    a. digital vein
    b. vena cava
    c. axillary vein
    d. brachial vein
    e. basilic vein

    Answer: d

41. At the level of the first rib, the axillary vein becomes the
    a. cephalic vein
    b. vena cava
    c. subclavian vein
    d. brachiocephalic vein
    e. external jugular vein

    Answer: c

42. The vein that is formed from the fusion of the subclavian with the internal and external jugulars is the
    a. vena cava
    b. axillary vein
    c. iliac vein
    d. hepatic vein
    e. brachiocephalic vein

    Answer: e

43. The fusion of the brachiocephalic veins forms the
    a. inferior vena cava
    b. superior vena cava
    c. brachiocephalic vein
    d. subclavian vein
    e. iliac vein

    Answer: b

44. The two common iliac veins form the
    a. femoral vein
    b. internal iliac vein
    c. external iliac vein
    d. lumbar vein
    e. common iliac vein

    Answer: c

45. Nutrients from the digestive tract enter the
    a. inferior vena
    b. superior vena cava
    c. hepatic vein
    d. hepatic vein
    e. renal vein

Answer: c

46. Elderly individuals usually have
    a. elevated hematocrits
    b. stiff inelastic arteries
    c. decreased blood pressure
    d. increased venous return

Answer: b

47. Elderly individuals are more prone to suffer from _____ than younger individuals.
    a. hypertension
    b. venous thrombosis
    c. arteriosclerosis
    d. problems with the conducting system of the heart
    e. all of the above

Answer: e

48. The kidneys release _____ in response to lowered blood pressure.
    a. renin
    b. erythropoietin
    c. ADH
    d. ACTH
    e. angiotensin

Answer: a

49. Factors that increase the risk of atherosclerosis include:
    a. smoking
    b. lack of exercise
    c. high fat diets
    d. obesity
    e. all of the above

Answer: e

50. Which of the following is greater?
    a. the normal blood volume of the arterial system
    b. the normal blood volume of the venous system

Answer: b

51. Which of the following would have the greater effect on peripheral resistance?
    a. doubling the length of a blood vessel
    b. decreasing the diameter by 1/2

    Answer: b

52. In which of the following would the resistance be greater?
    a. a vessel 10 microns in diameter
    b. a vessel 1 mm in diameter

    Answer: a

53. In which of the following would the rate of blood flow be lower?
    a. a vessel 10 microns in diameter
    b. a vessel 1 mm in diameter

    Answer: b

54. Each of the following factors would increase cardiac output **except** one. Identify the exception.
    a. increased venous return
    b. decreased parasympathetic stimulation of the heart
    c. increased sympathetic stimulation of the heart
    d. stimulation of the heart by epinephrine
    e. all of the above

    Answer: e

55. Which of the following is faster?
    a. blood flow along the walls of a blood vessel
    b. blood flow in the center of a large vessel

    Answer: b

56. Edema would be likely to form when
    a. the concentration of protein in the blood increases
    b. hemorrhage occurs
    c. the heart is an insufficient pump
    d. blood hydrostatic pressure at the capillary decreases
    e. the blood hydrostatic pressure in a capillary is equal to the blood osmotic pressure

    Answer: c

57. Which of the following is greater?
    a. the osmotic pressure of the interstitial fluid during inflammation
    b. the osmotic pressure of the interstitial fluid under normal conditions

    Answer: a

58. Which of the following is greater?
    a. blood pressure when sympathetic stimulation to the heart increases
    b. blood pressure when parasympathetic stimulation to the heart increases

    Answer: a

59. Which of the following is greater?
    a. heart rate normally
    b. heart rate during circulatory shock

    Answer: b

60. Which of the following is greater?
    a. blood pressure when the peripheral vessels dilate
    b. blood pressure when the peripheral vessels constrict

    Answer: b

61. Vicki has a tumor that causes her to secrete excess amounts of the hormone ADH. Because of the elevated level of hormone, she exhibits
    a. decreased blood volume
    b. increased blood pressure
    c. peripheral vasoconstriction
    d. increased numbers of red blood cells
    e. all of the above

    Answer: b

62. The vessels that permit exchange of materials between the cells and the blood are termed
    a. capillaries
    b. arterioles
    c. arteries
    d. venules
    e. veins

    Answer: a

63. Blood flow into capillaries is regulated by
    a. intercellular chemicals
    b. dilation of capillaries
    c. arterioles
    d. venules
    e. constriction of capillaries

    Answer: c

64. Transport mechanisms used by capillaries include:
   a. diffusion
   b. filtration
   c. osmosis
   d. A, B, and C
   e. none of the above

   Answer: d

65. Blood pressure is highest in which of the following structures?
   a. arteriole
   b. artery
   c. capillary
   d. vein
   e. venule

   Answer: b

66. Oxygen and carbon dioxide are transported across the capillary membrane by
   a. active transport
   b. diffusion
   c. osmosis
   d. hydrostatic pressure
   e. capsular pressure

   Answer: b

67. Swelling of a tissue is due to
   a. trauma to the blood
   b. constriction of vessels
   c. release of bone fragments
   d. increased permeability of capillaries
   e. filtration

   Answer: d

68. Pulse pressure is the difference between
   a. the heart at rest and the heart beat
   b. elastic rebound and elastic recoil
   c. circulatory pressure and blood pressure
   d. blood pressure and osmotic pressure
   e. systolic pressure and diastolic pressure

   Answer: e

69. Factors that influence blood pressure include all of the following **except**:
    a. heart action
    b. number of arterioles
    c. blood volume
    d. viscosity
    e. peripheral resistance

    Answer: b

Matching

70. Match the arteries in the first column with the major regions they supply in the second column.

    _____1. internal carotid   A. posterior abdominal wall
    _____2. phrenic   B. upper digestive tract
    _____3. renal   C. brain
    _____4. celiac   D. diaphragm
    _____5. lumbar   E. kidney

    Answer: 1-c, 2-d, 3-e, 4-b, 5-a

71. Match the veins in the first column with the major regions they supply in the second column.

    _____1. anterior tibial   A. external iliac
    _____2. femoral   B. femoral
    _____3. popliteal   C. subclavian
    _____4. basilic   D. axillary
    _____5. external jugular   E. popliteal

    Answer: 1-e, 2-a, 3-b, 4-d, 5-c

Fill-In-The-Blank

Supply the name of the missing <u>artery</u> in the sequence given.

72. common iliac artery, internal iliac artery, external iliac artery,
    _____ _____

    Answer: femoral artery

73. popliteal artery, _____ _____ _____, posterior tibial artery, peroneal arteries

    Answer: anterior tibial artery

74. _____ _____, aortic arch, thoracic aorta

    Answer: ascending aorta

75. descending aorta, _____ _____, abdominal aorta

    Answer: thoracic aorta

76. brachiocephalic artery, _____ _____ _____, external carotid artery

    Answer: common carotid artery

Supply the name of the missing <u>vein</u> in the sequence given.

77. right axillary vein, _____ _____, right brachiocephalic

    Answer: subclavian vein

78. left internal iliac, _____ _____ _____, inferior vena cava

    Answer: common iliac vein

79. great saphenous vein, external iliac vein, _____ _____ _____

    Answer: common iliac vein

80. inferior vena cava, _____ _____, liver

    Answer: hepatic vein

81. cephalic vein, subclavian vein, _____ _____

    Answer: brachiocephalic vein

82. _____ is the regulation of blood flow at the tissue level.

    Answer: Autoregulation

83. _____ _____ drain fluid from the interstitial spaces back into the general circulation.

    Answer: Lymphatic vessels

84. The term _____ _____ refers to the pressure in the arterial side of the circulatory system.

Answer: blood pressure

85. _____ _____ _____ refers to the factors that oppose blood flow in the circulatory system

Answer: Total peripheral resistance

86. In _____, the wall of an artery becomes thicker and tougher.

Answer: arteriosclerosis

87. The condition known as _____ is characterized by the formation of fatty plaques in the lining of arteries.

Answer: atherosclerosis

88. _____ _____ are the distinctive sounds heard during the measurement of blood pressure.

Answer: Karotkoff's sounds

89. The instrument used to determine blood pressure is the _____.

Answer: sphygmomanometer

90. The vessel that carries blood to the arm and shoulder is called the _____ _____.

Answer: subclavian artery

91. The vessel that supplies blood to the head and neck is the _____ _____ _____.

Answer: common carotid artery

92. The vessel that branches to form a right common carotid and a right subclavian artery is called the _____ _____.

Answer: innominate artery

93. This vessel that supplies blood to the upper arm is called the _____ _____.

Answer: brachial artery

94. This vessel that supplies blood to the brain and spinal cord is called the _____ _____.

    Answer: vertebral artery

95. This vessel that supplies blood to the liver, stomach, and spleen is called the _____ _____.

    Answer: celiac artery

96. This vessel that supplies blood to the pancreas, small intestine, and most of the large intestine is called the _____ _____ _____.

    Answer: superior mesenteric artery

97. The vessel that supplies blood to the arm and shoulder is the _____ _____.

    Answer: subclavian artery

98. The vessel that branches to form a right common carotid artery and a right subclavian artery is the _____ _____.

    Answer: innominate artery or brachiocephalic artery

99. The vessel that supplies blood to the muscles of the upper arm is the _____ _____.

    Answer: brachial artery

100. The small intestine and most of the large intestine receive blood from the _____ _____ _____.

    Answer: superior mesenteric artery

101. The lower part of the large intestine, including the rectum, receives blood from the _____ _____ _____.

    Answer: inferior mesenteric artery

102. Ovaries or testes receive a blood supply from the _____ _____.

    Answer: gonadal arteries

103. The kidneys receive blood from the _____ _____.

    Answer: renal arteries

104. The branch of the common iliac artery that serves the leg is the
_____ _____ _____.

Answer: external iliac artery

105. The vessel that collects blood from the overlying structures of the head and neck is the _____ _____ _____.

Answer: external jugular vein

106. Blood from the inside of the cranium is drained by the _____
_____ _____.

Answer: internal jugular vein

107. The _____ _____ receives blood from the kidney.

Answer: renal vein

108. Blood is drained from the liver by the _____ _____.

Answer: hepatic vein

109. Blood from inside the cranium is drained by the _____ _____
_____.

Answer: internal jugular vein

Essay

110. Tom loves to soak in hot tubs and whirlpools. One day, he decides to raise the temperature in his hot tub as high as it will go. After a few minutes in the very warm water, he feels faint, passes out, and nearly drowns. Luckily, he is saved by an observant bystander. Explain what happened physiologically.

Answer:
In response to the high temperature of the water, Tom's body shunted more blood to the superficial veins to decrease body temperature. The dilation of the superficial veins caused a shift in blood to the arms and legs and resulted in a decreased venous return. Because of the decreased venous return, the cardiac output decreased and less blood with oxygen was delivered to the brain. This caused Tom to feel light headed and faint, nearly causing his demise.

Chapter 15:   The Lymphatic System and Immunity

Multiple Choice

1. The lymphatic system is composed of
   a. lymphatic vessels
   b. lymph nodes
   c. the spleen
   d. a and b only
   e. all of the above

   Answer: e

2. The primary function of the lymphatic system is
   a. circulation of nutrients
   b. the transport of hormones
   c. the production, maintenance, and distribution of lymphocytes
   d. the production, maintenance, and distribution of plasma proteins
   e. all of the above

   Answer: c

3. The lymphatic system
   a. helps maintain normal blood volume
   b. fights infection
   c. eliminates variations in the composition of interstitial fluid
   d. transports lipids from the digestive tract
   e. all of the above

   Answer: e

4. Anatomically, lymph vessels resemble
   a. elastic arteries
   b. arterioles
   c. the vena cava
   d. veins
   e. muscular arteries

   Answer: d

5. Most of the lymph returns to the venous circulation by way of the
   a. right lymphatic duct
   b. thoracic duct
   c. inferior vena cava
   d. superior vena cava
   e. dural sinus

   Answer: b

6. The thoracic duct drains lymph from the
   a. left side of the head
   b. left side of the thorax
   c. left arm and shoulder
   d. body regions below the diaphragm
   e. all of the above

   Answer: e

7. Lymph nodes
   a. produce antibodies from specialized T cells
   b. monitor the contents of lymph, removing debris and pathogens
   c. act as a "way station" for cancer cells
   d. b and c only
   e. all of the above

   Answer: d

8. In general, lymphocytes
   a. spend little time in the blood
   b. have relatively long life-spans
   c. are not evenly distributed in the lymphatic tissues
   d. b and c only
   e. all of the above

   Answer: e

9. The cells known as lymphocytes
   a. are actively phagocytic
   b. destroy red blood cells
   c. produce proteins called antibodies
   d. are primarily found in red bone marrow
   e. decrease in number during infection

   Answer: c

10. Lymphocytes are located in each of the following tissues or organs
    except one. Identify the exception.
    a. tonsils
    b. spleen
    c. lymph nodes
    d. brain
    e. thymus gland

    Answer: d

11. _____ are large lymphatic nodules that are located in the walls of the pharynx.
    a. Tonsils
    b. Peyer's patches
    c. Lymph nodes
    d. Complements
    e. Spleens

    Answer: a

12. Areas of the spleen that contain large numbers of lymphoid nodules are known as
    a. Peyer's patches
    b. adenoids
    c. white pulp
    d. red pulp
    e. lymph nodes

    Answer: c

13. The red pulp of the spleen contains large numbers of
    a. red blood cells
    b. macrophages
    c. lymphocytes
    d. neutrophils
    e. antibodies

    Answer: a

14. Lymphatic organs are different from lymphatic tissues in that lymphatic organs
    a. contain lymphocytes and lymphatic tissues do not
    b. are found in the digestive tract and lymphatic tissues are found in the thorax
    c. are separated from surrounding tissues by a fibrous capsule and lymphatic tissues are not
    d. a and c only
    e. all of the above

    Answer: c

15. The largest collection of lymphatic tissue in the adult body is located in the
    a. liver
    b. thymus
    c. tonsils
    d. spleen
    e. lymph nodes

    Answer: d

16. The white pulp of the spleen is composed primarily of
    a. lymphocytes
    b. neutrophils
    c. red blood cells
    d. platelets
    e. fibrous connective tissue

Answer: a

17. The body's nonspecific defenses include
    a. skin
    b. complement
    c. interferon
    d. inflammation
    e. all of the above

Answer: e

18. Each of the following is a physical barrier **except** one. Identify the exception.
    a. hair
    b. epithelium
    c. secretions
    d. complement
    e. basement membranes

Answer: d

19. Immunological surveillance involves which of the following cells
    a. memory T cells
    b. memory B cells
    c. NK cells
    d. plasma cells
    e. monocytes

Answer: c

20. Interferons may be described as
    a. products of activated lymphocytes and macrophages
    b. antiviral substances
    c. an example of cytokines
    d. coordinators of local defense activities
    e. all of the above

Answer: e

21. Characteristics of specific defenses include
    a. versatility
    b. tolerance
    c. memory
    d. specificity
    e. all of the above

    Answer: e

22. Defense of the body against a particular bacteria or virus is provided
    by
    a. complement
    b. immunity
    c. interferon
    d. immunological surveillance
    e. fever

    Answer: b

23. The first line of cellular defense against pathogens are
    a. T cells
    b. B cells
    c. NK cells
    d. phagocytes
    e. plasma cells

    Answer: d

24. Microphages include
    a. microglia
    b. monocytes
    c. neutrophils
    d. lymphocytes
    e. all of the above

    Answer: c

25. All of the various macrophages are derived from
    a. lymphocytes
    b. monocytes
    c. neutrophils
    d. basophils
    e. eosinophils

    Answer: b

26. An inflammatory response is triggered when
    a. red blood cells release pus-forming agents
    b. T cells release interferon
    c. mast cells release histamine, serotonin, and heparin
    d. neutrophils phagocytize bacteria
    e. blood flow to an area increases

Answer: c

27. Immunity that results from the natural exposure to an antigen in the environment is called
    a. active natural
    b. passive natural
    c. innate
    d. active artificial
    e. autoimmunity

Answer: a

28. Immunity that results from antibodies that pass the placenta from mother to fetus is called
    a. active natural
    b. passive natural
    c. innate
    d. active artificial
    e. autoimmunity

Answer: b

29. In active artificial immunity
    a. the immune system attacks normal body cells
    b. the body is deliberately exposed to an antigen
    c. the body receives antibodies produced by another person
    d. the body receives antibodies produced by another animal
    e. genes for antibodies are introduced into the body

Answer: b

30. The cells responsible for the production of circulating antibodies are
    a. NK cells
    b. plasma cells
    c. helper T cells
    d. cytotoxic T cells
    e. suppressor T cells

Answer: b

31. The cells responsible for humoral immunity are the
    a. NK cells
    b. B cells
    c. helper T cells
    d. cytotoxic T cells
    e. suppressor T cells

    Answer: b

32. Cells that help to regulate the immune response are
    a. B cells
    b. plasma cells
    c. helper T cells
    d. cytotoxic cells
    e. NK cells

    Answer: c

33. Suppressor T cells act to
    a. suppress antigens
    b. limit the degree of memory in memory T cells
    c. limit antigen proliferation
    d. depress the responses of other T cells and B cells
    e. produce antibodies involved in autoimmunity

    Answer: d

34. The cells that are actively involved in immunological surveillance are the
    a. NK cells
    b. plasma cells
    c. B cells
    d. helper T cels
    e. suppressor T cells

    Answer: a

35. Stem cells that will form T cells are modified in the
    a. bone marrow
    b. liver
    c. spleen
    d. thymus
    e. kidneys

    Answer: d

36. The various classes of immunoglobulins are differentiated on the basis of their
    a. shapes
    b. affinity for antigens
    c. variable regions
    d. fixed segments
    e. all of the above

    Answer: d

37. Immunoglobulins that are the largest class and are mainly responsible for resistance against viruses, bacteria, and bacterial toxins are
    a. IgA
    b. IgD
    c. IgE
    d. IgG
    e. IgM

    Answer: d

38. Immunoglobulins that attach to mast cells and basophils and are involved in allergic reactions are
    a. IgA
    b. IgD
    c. IgE
    d. IgG
    e. IgM

    Answer: c

39. Immunoglobulins that are found on the surface of B cells and may play a role in regulation of the humoral immune response are
    a. IgA
    b. IgD
    c. IgE
    d. IgG
    e. IgM

    Answer: b

40. Immunoglobulins that are the first antibodies to be produced in response to infection are
    a. IgA
    b. IgD
    c. IgE
    d. IgG
    e. IgM

    Answer: e

41. Immunoglobulins that are primarily found in glandular secretions are
    a. IgA
    b. IgD
    c. IgE
    d. IgG
    e. IgM

    Answer: a

42. The specificity of an antibody is determined by the
    a. fixed segment
    b. antigenic determinants
    c. variable region
    d. size of the antibodies
    e. the antibody class

    Answer: c

43. The binding of an antigen to an antibody can result in
    a. neutralization of the antigen
    b. agglutination or precipitation
    c. complement activation
    d. destruction of the antigen
    e. all of the above

    Answer: e

44. In order for a lymphocyte to respond to an antigen, the antigen must
    a. be phagocytized by the lymphocyte
    b. enter the cytoplasm of the lymphocyte
    c. bind to the DNA of the lymphocyte
    d. bind to specific receptors on the lymphocyte membrane
    e. depolarize the lymphocyte membrane

    Answer: d

45. The role of accessory cells in immunity is to
    a. produce antibodies
    b. produce memory cells
    c. digest foreign cells and molecules and present antigens
    d. actively lyse bacterial cells
    e. coat pathogens with antigens

    Answer: c

46. The major histocompatibility complex (MHC)
    a. is responsible for forming lymphocytes
    b. produces antibodies in lymph glands
    c. is a group of genes that codes for human leukocyte antigens
    d. is a membrane protein that can recognize foreign antigens
    e. is the antigen found on bacteria that stimulates an immune response

Answer: d

47. B cells are primarily activated by the activities of
    a. antigens
    b. antibodies
    c. helper T cells
    d. macrophages
    e. plasma cells

Answer: c

48. The following are steps in the cell-mediated immune response.
    1. several cycles of mitosis occur
    2. antigen is engulfed and presented by a macrophage
    3. cytotoxic T cells migrate to focus of infection
    4. undifferentiated T cells with specific receptors recognize the antigen
    5. T cells differentiate into cytotoxic T cells and T memory cells
    6. cytotoxic T cells release toxins

    The correct sequence for these steps is
    a. 4, 1, 5, 3, 6, 2
    b. 2, 4, 1, 5, 3, 6
    c. 1, 2, 4, 5, 3, 6
    d. 3, 2, 4, 1, 5, 6
    e. 3, 6, 4, 5, 1, 2

Answer: b

49. Newborn infants gain most of their immunity from
    a. early immunizations
    b. contact with viruses and bacteria
    c. antibodies passed from the mother across the placenta
    d. contact with siblings
    e. innate factors

Answer: c

50. The largest class of antibodies, with several subtypes is:
    a. IgA
    b. IgD
    c. IgE
    d. IgG
    e. IgM

    Answer: d

51. Autoantibodies
    a. are produced by activated T-cells
    b. are produced during an allergic reaction
    c. function against the body's normal antigens
    d. are produced during immunodeficiency diseases
    e. all of the above

    Answer: c

52. Inappropriate or excessive immune responses to antigens are
    a. immunodeficiency diseases
    b. autoimmune diseases
    c. allergies
    d. the result of stress
    e. common in the elderly

    Answer: c

53. Changes in the immune system that accompany aging include
    a. T cells becoming less responsive to antigens
    b. more cytotoxic T cells responding to infections
    c. increased numbers of T helper cells
    d. higher levels of antibody after initial exposure to antigens
    e. all of the above

    Answer: a

54. Histamine increases blood flow and vascular permeability. This would account for which of the following changes that occur during inflammation?
    a. redness of the inflamed tissue
    b. swelling of the inflamed tissue
    c. heat of the inflamed tissue
    d. the localization of proteins and cells necessary for body defense
    e. all of the above

    Answer: e

55. In an experimental situation, a virus is injected into a rabbit and the rabbit is allowed to make antibodies for the viral antigen. These antibodies are then removed from the rabbit plasma and injected into a human to help deal with the same viral disease. This would be an example of
    a. innate immunity
    b. active immunization
    c. passive immunization
    d. natural immunity
    e. autoimmunity

Answer: c

56. Blocking the antigen receptors on the surface of lymphocytes would interfere with
    a. phagocytosis of the antigen
    b. that lymphocyte's ability to produce antibodies
    c. antigen recognition
    d. the ability of the lymphocyte to present antigen
    e. agglutination of the antigen

Answer: c

57. A decrease in which population of lymphocytes would impair all aspects of an immune response?
    a. cytotoxic T cells
    b. helper T cells
    c. suppressor T cells
    d. B cells
    e. plasma cells

Answer: b

58. The human immunodeficiency virus (HIV) that causes the disease known as AIDS selectively infects
    a. B cells
    b. Plasma cells
    c. cytotoxic T cells
    d. helper T cells
    e. suppressor T cells

Answer: d

59. Infection with the HIV virus occurs through
    a. eating contaminated food
    b. airborne droplets from coughs and sneezes
    c. intimate contact with an infected person's body fluids
    d. casual contact with an infected individual
    e. all of the above

Answer: c

60. A fluid sample contains a large amount of IgA-type antibody. This fluid is probably
    a. lymph
    b. blood
    c. serum
    d. tears
    e. saliva

    Answer: d

61. Lymph re-enters the venous system at:
    a. the right and left subclavian veins
    b. lymph nodes
    c. the thoracic duct
    d. the intestinal tract
    e. the vena cava

    Answer: a

62. Functions of the lymphatic system include all of the following **except**:
    a. production of lymphocytes
    b. return of solutes from peripheral tissues to the blood
    c. formation of tissue fluid
    d. distribution of hormones from their tissue of origin to the general circulation
    e. distribution of lymphocytes

    Answer: c

63. Lymph nodules are comprised of loose connective tissue containing densely packed
    a. Peyer's patches
    b. basophils
    c. spleens
    d. neutrophils
    e. lymphocytes

    Answer: e

64. A bacterial infection in the foot would most likely affect lymph nodes in which of the following regions?
    a. axillary
    b. cervical
    c. mammary
    d. inguinal
    e. brachial

    Answer: d

65. The thymus gland is positioned
    a. posterior to the thyroid gland
    b. just behind the sternum
    c. inferior to the heart
    d. posterior to the trachea
    e. in the inguinal region

Answer: b

66. Major events associated with swelling include:
    a. redness, swelling, heat, and pain
    b. redness, pus, fever, and rapid heart rate
    c. tears, swelling, pain, and fever
    d. inflammation, redness, tissue damage, and altered pH
    e. heat, pain, fever, and activation of the complement system

Answer: a

67. Identify the false statement regarding the thymus gland.
    a. It is the site of T-cell maturation.
    b. After puberty, the gland begins to atrophy.
    c. The thymus gland has several lobes.
    d. Lymphocytes in the cortex divide.
    e. Thymosins within the structure produce thymic hormones.

Answer: c

68. Identify the false statement regarding the spleen.
    a. it contains the largest collection of lymphatic tissue in the body.
    b. It is located in the lower quadrant of the pelvic cavity.
    c. Macrophages located in the structure play a vital role in immunity.
    d. It removes abnormal blood cells from the circulation.
    e. It initiates immune responses by B cells and T cells.

Answer: b

69. This immunoglobulin is responsible for defense against many viruses, bacteria, and bacterial toxins.
    a. IgA
    b. IgD
    c. IgE
    d. IgG
    e. IgM

Answer: d

70. This immunoglobulin functions to attack bacteria insensitive to IgG.
    a. IgA
    b. IgD
    c. IgE
    d. IgF
    e. IgM

    Answer: e

71. The function of this immunoglobulin is to attack pathogens before they enter body tissues.
    a. IgA
    b. IgD
    c. IgE
    d. IgF
    e. IgM

    Answer: a

72. The chemical mediators responsible for killing tumor cells, stimulating T cell activity, and inhibiting parasites and viruses are termed:
    a. interleukins
    b. interferons
    c. tumor necrosis factors
    d. phagocytic regulators
    e. colony-stimulating factors

    Answer: c

73. This class of chemical mediators stimulates the production of both microphages and monocytes.
    a. Il-1
    b. Il-2
    c. MIF
    d. M-CSF
    e. GM-CSF

    Answer: e

74. One of the most common cancers seen in AIDS patients is
    a. small cell carcinoma
    b. Kaposi's sarcoma
    c. malignant neoplasm
    d. lung cancer
    e. bone cancer

    Answer: b

75. With advancing age, the immune system
    a. becomes more effective at combating disease
    b. remains the same and is not affected by the aging process
    c. has alternating periods of efficacy
    d. becomes less effective at combating disease
    e. becomes more responsive to antigens

    Answer: d

76. The increased incidence of cancer in the elderly reflects the fact that
    a. immune surveillance increases
    b. tumor cells are eliminated effectively
    c. their diets do not meet nutritional standards
    d. everyone is prone to disease
    e. immune surveillance declines with age

    Answer: e

Fill-In-The-Blank

77. The larger of the two collecting ducts is the _____ duct.

    Answer: thoracic

78. The functional units of lymph nodes are called _____.

    Answer: nodules

79. Lymph enters a lymph node through the _____ vessel and exits it via the _____ vessel.

    Answer: afferent; efferent

80. _____ tissues are connective tissues dominated by lymphocytes.

    Answer: Lymphatic

81. The body's diffuse collection of phagocytic cells is sometimes called the _____ _____.

    Answer: monocyte-macrophage system

82. _____ _____ are phagocytic cells that are permanent residents of specific tissues and organs.

    Answer: Fixed macrophages

83. _____ _____ attracts monocytes and activates them to macrophages.

    Answer: Monocyte-chemotactic factor (MCF)

84. The ability of certain phagocytes to move through the wall of a capillary is called _____.

   Answer: diapedesis

85. The ability of certain cells to respond to changes in their chemical environment is called _____.

   Answer: chemotaxis

86. Any compound that can stimulate the body to produce antibodies is called a(n) _____.

   Answer: antigen

87. _____ are antibodies found in body fluids.

   Answer: Immunoglobulins

88. The portions of an antigen that are recognized by an antibody are the _____ _____ _____.

   Answer: antigenic determinant sites

89. When an antibody binds to its proper antigen a(n) _____ _____ _____ is formed.

   Answer: antigen-antibody complex

90. _____ _____ is the ability to demonstrate an immune response upon exposure to an antigen.

   Answer: Immunological competence

91. _____ cells enable the immune system to respond more quickly if the same antigen is encountered a second time.

   Answer: Memory

92. _____ exists when the immune system does not respond to a particular antigen.

   Answer: Tolerance

93. _____ disorders develop when the immune response mistakenly targets normal body cells.

   Answer: autoimmune

94. Antigens that trigger allergic reactions are called _____.

    Answer: allergens

Essay

95. Paula's grandfather is diagnosed as having lung cancer. His physician orders biopsies of several lymph nodes from neighboring regions of the body, and Paula wonders why, since his cancer is in the lungs. What would you tell her?

    Answer:
    A key characteristic of cancer cells is their ability to break free from a tumor and migrate to other tissues of the body forming new tumors. This process is called metastasis. The primary route for the spread of cancer cells is the lymphatic system, and cancer cells may remain in a lymph node for a period of time before moving on to other tissues. Examination of regional lymph nodes for the presence of cancer cells can help the physician determine if the cancer was caught in an early stage or whether it has started to spread to other tissues. It can also give the physician an idea of what other tissues may be affected by the cancer, which would help in deciding on the proper treatment.

96. Willy is allergic to ragweed pollen and tells you that he read about a medication that can help his condition by blocking certain antibodies. Do you think that this treatment could help Willy? Explain.

    Answer:
    Allergies occur when antigens called allergens bind to specific IgE type antibodies that are bound to the surface of mast cells and basophils. A person becomes allergic when they develop IgE antibodies for a specific allergen. Theoretically at least, a molecule that would bind to the specific IgE for ragweed allergen and prevent the allergen from binding should help to relieve the allergy.

97. Mrs. Smith is a 50-year old woman who has just had a radical mastectomy. Several days following the surgery, she notices that her arm is swollen and painful. Explain why she may be experiencing lymphedema in her sore arm.

    Answer:
    It is possible that the remaining lymph nodes are not able to adequately handle the lymph flow, thus this is causing an increase in hydrostatic pressure. Although the swelling could be due to an infection, the most probable cause would be from the removal of lymph glands surrounding the excised breast tissue. This would in turn compromise lymph flow, causing a build-up of lymph drainage and leakage into the interstitial spaces, thereby creating lymphedema.

Chapter 16:   The Respiratory System

Multiple Choice

1. Functions of the respiratory system include
   a. protecting respiratory surfaces from dehydration, temperature changes, or other environmental variations
   b. defending the respiratory system and other tissues from pathogenic invasion
   c. providing an extensive area for gas exchange between air and circulating blood
   d. a and c only
   e. all of the above

   Answer: e *d*

2. Air entering the body is filtered, warmed, and humidified by the
   a. upper respiratory tract
   b. lower respiratory tract
   c. lungs
   d. alveoli
   e. all of the above

   Answer: a

3. Large airborne particles are filtered by the
   a. external olfactory meatuses
   b. the soft palate
   c. nasal hairs in the vestibule of the nose
   d. the nasal sinuses
   e. the nasopharynx

   Answer: c

4. Surfactant
   a. protects the surface of the lungs
   b. phagocytizes small particulates
   c. replaces mucus in the alveoli
   d. helps prevent the alveoli from collapsing
   e. is not found in healthy lung tissue

   Answer: d

5. The function of the nasal conchae is
   a. to divide the nasal cavity into a right and a left side
   b. to provide an opening into the pharynx
   c. to provide a surface for the sense of smell
   d. to create turbulence in the air so as to trap small particulates in mucus
   e. to provide an opening to the outside of the body

   Answer: d

6. Functions of the nose include
   a. filtering the air
   b. warming the air
   c. humidifying the air
   d. acting as a resonating chamber in speech
   e. all of the above

   Answer: e

7. The openings to the nostrils are the
   a. external nares
   b. internal nares
   c. vestibules
   d. turbinates
   e. palates

   Answer: a

8. The portion of the nasal cavity contained within the flexible tissues of
   the external nose is the
   a. nasopharynx
   b. vestibule
   c. internal chamber
   d. glottis
   e. nasal septum

   Answer: b

9. The portion of the pharynx that receives both air and food is the
   a. nasopharynx
   b. oropharynx
   c. laryngopharynx
   d. vestibule
   e. internal pharynx

   Answer: b

10. The common passageway shared by the respiratory and digestive systems is
    the
    a. larynx
    b. glottis
    c. vestibule
    d. pharynx
    e. trachea

    Answer: d

11. The hard palate separates
    a. the nasal cavity from the larynx
    b. the left and right sides of the nasal cavity
    c. the nasal cavity and the oral cavity
    d. the external nares from the internal nares
    e. the soft palate from the nasal cavity

    Answer: c

12. The openings to the Eustachian tube are located in the
    a. nasopharynx
    b. oropharynx
    c. laryngopharynx
    d. larynx
    e. nasal cavity

    Answer: a

13. The palatine tonsils lie in the walls of the
    a. nasopharynx
    b. oropharynx
    c. laryngopharynx
    d. larynx
    e. nasal cavity

    Answer: b

14. The glottis is
    a. the inferior margin of the soft palate
    b. a flap of elastic cartilage
    c. the opening to the larynx
    d. the opening to the pharynx
    e. part of the hard palate

    Answer: c

15. The vocal folds are located in the
    a. nasopharynx
    b. oropharynx
    c. larynx
    d. trachea
    e. bronchi

    Answer: c

16. The elastic cartilage that shields the opening to the larynx during swallowing is the
    a. thyroid cartilage
    b. cricoid cartilage
    c. corniculate cartilage
    d. cuneiform cartilage
    e. epiglottic cartilage

Answer: e

17. The cartilage that makes up most of the anterior and lateral surface of the larynx is the
    a. thyroid cartilage
    b. cricoid cartilage
    c. cuneiform cartilage
    d. arytenoid cartilage
    e. epiglottic cartilage

Answer: a

18. The cartilage that serves as a base for the larynx is
    a. thyroid cartilage
    b. cuneiform cartilage
    c. corniculate cartilage
    d. cricoid cartilage
    e. arytenoid cartilage

Answer: d

19. The trachea
    a. is lined by pseudostratified ciliated columnar epithelium
    b. is reinforced with C-shaped cartilages
    c. contains many mucous glands
    d. can alter its diameter when stimulated by the autonomic nervous system
    e. all of the above

Answer: e

20. The airway between the larynx and the primary bronchi is the
    a. pharynx
    b. bronchiole
    c. trachea
    d. alveolar duct
    e. laryngeal duct

Answer: c

21. Secondary bronchi supply air to the
    a. lungs
    b. lobes of the lungs
    c. lobules of the lungs
    d. alveoli
    e. alveolar ducts

    Answer: b

22. Structures formed by the branching of the trachea within the mediastinum
    are
    a. secondary bronchi
    b. bronchioles
    c. tertiary bronchi
    d. primary bronchi
    e. alveoli

    Answer: d

23. The following is a list of some of the structures of the respiratory
    tree.
    1. secondary bronchi
    2. bronchioles
    3. alveolar ducts
    4. primary bronchi
    5. respiratory bronchioles
    6. alveoli
    7. terminal bronchioles

    The order in which air passes through these structures beginning at
    the trachea is:
    a. 4,1,2,7,5,3,6
    b. 4,1,2,5,7,3,6
    c. 1,4,2,5,7,3,6
    d. 1,4,2,7,5,3,6
    e. 2,4,1,7,5,3,6

    Answer: a

24. The respiratory membrane consists primarily of
    a. pseudostratified ciliated columnar epithelium
    b. moist cuboidal epithelium
    c. simple squamous epithelium
    d. ciliated squamous epithelium
    e. surfactant cells

    Answer: c

25. The actual sites of gas exchange within the lungs are
    a. bronchioles
    b. alveolar ducts
    c. pleural spaces
    d. alveoli
    e. terminal sacs

    Answer: d

26. Gas volume is
    a. directly proportional to pressure
    b. directly proportional to temperature
    c. indirectly proportional to pressure
    d. indirectly proportional to temperature
    e. b and c are correct

    Answer: e

27. Air moves into the lungs because
    a. the gas pressure in the lungs is less than outside pressure
    b. the volume of the lungs decreases with inspiration
    c. the thorax is muscular
    d. contraction of the diaphragm decreases the volume of the pleural
       cavity
    e. all of the above

    Answer: a

28. Air moves out of the lungs because
    a. the gas pressure in the lungs is less than outside pressure
    b. the volume of the lungs decreases with expiration
    c. contraction of the diaphragm increases the volume of the pleural
       cavity
    d. a and c only
    e. all of the above

    Answer: b

29. Expiratory movements are produced by contraction of the
    a. scalenes
    b. diaphragm
    c. internal intercostals
    d. external intercostals
    e. serratus anterior

    Answer: c

30. When the diaphragm and external intercostal muscles contract
    a. the volume of the thoracic cavity increases
    b. the volume of the thoracic cavity decreases
    c. the volume of the lungs decreases
    d. the lungs collapse
    e. expiration occurs

Answer: a

31. Pulmonary ventilation refers to
    a. the movement of air into and out of the lungs
    b. the movement of dissolved gases from the alveoli to the blood
    c. the movement of dissolved gases from the blood to the interstitial space
    d. the movement of dissolved gases from the interstitial space to the cells
    e. the utilization of oxygen

Answer: a

32. Alveolar ventilation refers to
    a. the movement of air into and out of the lungs
    b. the movement of air into and out of the alveoli
    c. the movement of dissolved gases from the alveoli to the blood
    d. the movement of dissolved gases from the blood to the alveoli
    e. the utilization of oxygen by alveolar cells to support metabolism

Answer: b

33. The function of pulmonary ventilation is to
    a. remove carbon dioxide from the lymph
    b. supply nitrogen to the blood
    c. maintain an adequate alveolar ventilation
    d. remove air from dead air space
    e. prevent gas exchange in the bronchioles

Answer: c

34. The process by which dissolved gases are exchanged between the blood and interstitial fluids is
    a. pulmonary ventilation
    b. external respiration
    c. internal respiration
    d. cellular respiration
    e. breathing

Answer: c

35. Most of the oxygen transported by the blood is
    a. dissolved in plasma
    b. bound to hemoglobin
    c. in ionic form as solute in the plasma
    d. bound to the same protein as carbon dioxide
    e. carried by white blood cells

    Answer: b

36. Most of the carbon dioxide in the blood is transported as
    a. solute dissolved in the plasma
    b. carbaminohemoglobin
    c. bicarbonate ions
    d. solute dissolved in the cytoplasm of red blood cells
    e. carbonic acid

    Answer: c

37. The most important chemical regulator of respiration is
    a. oxygen
    b. carbon dioxide
    c. bicarbonate ion
    d. sodium ion
    e. hemoglobin

    Answer: b

38. A 10% increase in the level of carbon dioxide in the blood will
    a. decrease the rate of breathing
    b. increase the rate of breathing
    c. decrease pulmonary ventilation
    d. decrease the alveolar ventilation rate
    e. decrease the vital capacity

    Answer: b

39. The average respiratory rate in a normal adult is
    a. less than 10 per minute
    b. 12 to 18 per minute
    c. 20 to 25 per minute
    d. 30 per minute
    e. none of the above

    Answer: b

40. The normal rate and depth of breathing is established by the
    a. dorsal respiratory group
    b. inspiratory center
    c. ventral respiratory group
    d. expiratory center
    e. respiratory rhythmicity center

    Answer: e

41. Together, the inflation and deflation reflexes are known as the
    _____ reflexes
    a. red herring
    b. Hering-Breuer
    c. Breuer-Shipley
    d. baroreceptor
    e. inside angle

    Answer: b

42. The deflation reflex operates by
    a. inhibiting the expiratory center and stimulating the inspiratory
       center when the lungs are collapsing
    b. preventing overexpansion during forced breathing
    c. osmoreceptors located in the carotid sinus
    d. being activated during normal, quiet breathing
    e. preventing overexpansion during quiet breathing

    Answer: a

43. In quiet breathing
    a. inspiration and expiration involve muscular contractions
    b. inspiration is passive and expiration involves muscular contractions
    c. inspiration involves muscular contractions and expiration is passive
    d. inspiration and expiration are both passive processes
    e. none of the above

    Answer: c

44. External respiration involves
    a. the movement of air into and out of the lungs
    b. the diffusion of gases between the alveoli and the circulating blood
    c. the exchange of dissolved gases between the blood and the
       interstitial fluid
    d. the binding of oxygen by hemoglobin
    e. the utilization of oxygen by tissues to support metabolism

    Answer: b

45. The process of internal respiration involves each of the following steps **except** one. Identify the exception.
    a. Oxygen diffuses from the blood to the interstitial space.
    b. Carbon dioxide diffuses from the interstitial space to the blood.
    c. Hemoglobin binds more oxygen.
    d. Bicarbonate ions are formed in the red blood cells.
    e. Chloride ions diffuse into red blood cells as bicarbonate ions diffuse out.

Answer: c

46. If a student inhales as deeply as possible and then blows the air out until he cannot exhale any more, the amount of air that he expelled would be his/her
    a. tidal volume
    b. inspiratory reserve volume
    c. expiratory reserve volume
    d. minimal volume
    e. vital capacity

Answer: e

47. Which of the following factors would increase the amount of oxygen discharged by hemoglobin to peripheral tissues?
    a. decreased temperature
    b. decreased pH
    c. increased tissue P02
    d. none of the above
    e. all of the above

Answer: b

48. Who would have a higher pitched voice?
    a. a person with thick vocal folds
    b. a person with thin vocal folds

Answer: b

49. When speaking, only the first third of Joe's vocal folds vibrate, but when John speaks, half of the length of his vocal folds vibrates. Who has a higher pitched voice?
    a. Joe
    b. John

Answer: a

50. Which is greater?
    a. the number of lobes in the right lung
    b. the number of lobes in the left lung

Answer: a

51. When the diaphragm and external intercostal muscles contract
    a. expiration occurs
    b. intrapulmonary pressure increases
    c. intrapleural pressure decreases
    d. the volume of the lungs decreases
    e. all of the above

    Answer: c

52. Damage to the surfactant cells of the lungs would result in
    a. a thickening of the respiratory membrane
    b. an increased rate of gas exchange
    c. alveolar rupture
    d. alveolar collapse
    e. decreased surface tension in the water lining the alveoli

    Answer: d

53. Harry suffers from cystic fibrosis and frequently has periods where he can hardly breathe. The problem is probably the result of
    a. inflammation of the bronchi
    b. constriction of the trachea
    c. thick secretions that exceed the ability of the respiratory tract to remove them
    d. laryngospasms that occur in response to a toxic substance produced by the epithelial cells
    e. collapse of one or both lungs

    Answer: c

54. Lungs and airways that are inflated at birth normally do not collapse again because
    a. cartilages and connective tissues hold the airways open
    b. surfactant prevents the alveoli from collapsing
    c. negative intrathoracic pressure prevents total elastic recoil of the lungs
    d. b and c only
    e. all of the above

    Answer: e

55. Carbon dioxide is more soluble in water than oxygen. To get the same amount of oxygen to dissolve in plasma as carbon dioxide, you would have to
    a. increase the temperature of the plasma
    b. increase the partial pressure of oxygen
    c. decrease the partial pressure of oxygen
    d. increase the rate of plasma flow through the lungs
    e. decrease the alveolar ventilation rate

    Answer: b

56. Which of the following would be greater?
    a. the percent of oxygen saturation of hemoglobin when the pH is 7.6
    b. the percent of oxygen saturation of hemoglobin when the pH is 7.2

    Answer: a

57. Which of the following would be greater?
    a. the percent of oxygen saturation of hemoglobin when the temperature is 37 degrees Celsius
    b. the percent of oxygen saturation of hemoglobin when the temperature is 40 degrees Celsius

    Answer: b

58. Which of the following is greater?
    a. the partial pressure of oxygen in the alveoli
    b. the partial pressure of oxygen in expired air

    Answer: b

59. Which of the following is greater?
    a. the partial pressure of carbon dioxide in the alveoli
    b. the partial pressure of carbon dioxide in expired air

    Answer: a

60. With aging
    a. the lungs become more elastic
    b. the lungs become more compliant
    c. vital capacity increases
    d. pulmonary ventilation decreases
    e. costal cartilages become more flexible

    Answer: d

61. Katrina lives in St. Louis, which is close to sea level. She decides to spend a month of her summer vacation working in the mountains outside of Denver. After a week in the mountains, what kinds of changes would you expect to see as Katrina adapts to the higher altitude?
    a. decreased hematocrit
    b. decreased blood pressure
    c. decreased alveolar ventilation rate
    d. decreased P02 in the alveoli
    e. all of the above

    Answer: d

62. Kyley is singing a song. At a certain point in the song she forces a large volume of air out of the glottis and at the same time increases the tension on her vocal cords. The sound that she produces is
    a. low pitched and loud
    b. high pitched and loud
    c. low pitched and soft
    d. high pitched and soft
    e. medium pitched and soft

    Answer: b

63. In a condition known as pleurisy, there is excess fluid in the pleural space. How would you expect this to affect the process of pulmonary ventilation?
    a. ventilation would require less energy
    b. breathing would be labored and difficult
    c. it would be easier to expand the lungs on inspiration
    d. more air would be forced out during an expiration
    e. tidal volume would increase

    Answer: b

64. In emphysema, the alveoli break down and coalesce into large air spaces. The lungs also lose elasticity and compliance is increased. You would expect a person who suffers from emphysema to have
    a. increased dead air space
    b. decreased vital capacity
    c. elevated P_{CO_2} in the blood
    d. increased anteroposterior diameter of the thorax
    e. all of the above

    Answer: e

65. Identify the most common lethal inherited disease affecting Caucasians of Northern European descent that results from a defective gene located on chromosome 7.
    a. pneumonia
    b. emphysema
    c. cystic fibrosis
    d. asthma
    e. pneumothorax

    Answer: c

66. In individuals afflicted with CF, which of the following can occur?
    a. production of dense, viscous mucus
    b. interruption of mucus transport
    c. blockage of respiratory passageways
    d. frequent bacterial infections
    e. all of the above

    Answer: e

67. In this procedure, an incision is made through the anterior tracheal wall and a tube is inserted.
    a. tracheostomy
    b. tracheotomy
    c. bronchoscopy
    d. laryngotomy
    e. none of the above

Answer: b

68. The most common pneumonia that develops in AIDS patients results from infection by
    a. *Mycoplasma pneumoniae*
    b. *Haemophilus influenzae*
    c. *Klebsiella pneumoniae*
    d. *Pneumocystic carinii*
    e. *Mycobacterium tuberculosis*

Answer: d

69. Tuberculosis results from the colonization of which microorganism?
    a. *Mycoplasma pneumoniae*
    b. *Haemophilus influenzae*
    c. *Klebsiella pneumoniae*
    d. *Pneumocystic carinii*
    e. *Mycobacterium tuberculosis*

Answer: e

70. One measure of pulmonary function can be determined by a spirometer. This instrument measures:
    a. vital capacity
    b. maximum rate of air movement
    c. expiratory reserve
    d. inspiratory reserve
    e. A, C, and D

Answer: e

71. A device called a pneumotachometer measures:
    a. the rate of air movement
    b. the maximum rate of forced expiration
    c. expiratory reserve volume
    d. inspiratory reserve volume
    e. vital capacity

Answer: a

72. Decompression sickness is a painful condition that results in _____ gas coming out of solution in the bloodstream.
    a. oxygen
    b. hydrogen
    c. nitrogen
    d. A and B
    e. all of the above

    Answer: c

73. A chronic, progressive condition characterized by shortness of breath and destruction of alveolar surfaces and inadequate surface area for gaseous exchange is termed:
    a. cystic fibrosis
    b. emphysema
    c. asthma
    d. pneumonia
    e. none of the above

    Answer: b

74. The term _____ refers to an increase in the P_{CO_2} of arterial blood.
    a. hyperventilation
    b. hypoventilation
    c. hypocapnia
    d. hypercapnia
    e. hypoglycemia

    Answer: d

75. The following are distinguishing features of the glottis and epiglottis **except**:
    a. The glottis is an opening at the superior end of the trachea.
    b. The epiglottis is an opening at the superior end of the trachea.
    c. The epiglottis is a flap-like structure.
    d. The epiglottis shunts food away from the glottis during swallowing.
    e. all of the above are correct

    Answer: b

Matching

76. Match the structure in the first column with its description in the second column

       _____1. sinus
       _____2. surfactant
       _____3. pleura
       _____4. vital capacity
       _____5. inflation reflex

A. tidal volume, expiratory reserve volume, and inspiratory reserve volume
B. serous membrane
C. reduces the surface tension in the lungs
D. hollow chamber
E. prevents overexpansion of lungs during forced breathing

Answer: 1-d, 2-c, 3-b, 4-a, 5-e

Fill-In-The-Blank

77. _____ is the modification of sounds produced in the larynx by other structures to form recognizable words.

Answer: Articulation

78. The lungs are divided into _____ that are separated by deep fissures.

Answer: lobes

79. The condition in which there is an increase in the P_{CO_2} arterial blood is known as _____.

Answer: hypercapnia

80. When the inspiratory muscles relax, the rib cage returns to its original position as a result of _____ _____.

Answer: elastic recoil

81. The ease with which the lungs stretch in response to changes in pressure is termed _____.

Answer: compliance

82. The illness characterized by shortness of breath resulting from loss of respiratory membrane surface for gas exchange is _____.

Answer: emphysema

83. _____ is formed when carbon dioxide attaches to hemoglobin.

Answer: Carbaminohemoglobin

84. The _____ _____ _____ of the medulla oblongata sets the pace for inspiration.

    Answer: respiratory rhythmicity center

85. The _____ reflex prevents the lungs from over-expanding during forced breathing.

    Answer: inflation

86. Chemoreceptors located in the _____ bodies and _____ bodies are sensitive to changes in P_{CO_2} and P_{O_2}.

    Answer: carotid; aortic

87. An increase in the rate and depth of breathing is known as _____.

    Answer: hyperventilation

88. The volume of air moved into or out of the lungs during quiet respiration is known as _____ _____.

    Answer: tidal volume

89. The volume of air that can be forcefully expelled from the lungs following a normal exhalation is called the _____ _____ _____.

    Answer: expiratory reserve volume

90. The volume of air that can be forcefully inhaled on top of a normal inspiration is called the _____ _____ _____.

    Answer: inspiratory reserve volume

Essay

91. During the winter, Brad sleeps in a dorm room that lacks any humidifier for the heated air. In the mornings he notices that his nose is "stuffy" similar to when he has a cold, but after showering and drinking some water, the stuffiness disappears until the next morning. What might be the cause of Brad's nasal condition?

Answer:
Since the air that Brad is breathing is not humidified (thus dry), large amounts of moisture are leaving the mucus to humidify the air that is being respired. This makes the mucus tacky and difficult for the cilia to move. As more mucus is produced, it builds up forming the nasal congestion in the morning. As Brad showers and drinks fluid, the moisture is replaced and the mucus loosens up and is moved along the proper route as usual. The reason this happens mostly at night is because Brad is probably not getting up frequently to drink water to replace what is being lost to humidify the air.

92. A newborn infant is found dead, abandoned by the road. Among the many questions that the police would like to have answered is whether the infant was born dead or alive. After an autopsy, the medical examiner tells them that the infant was dead at birth. How could the medical examiner determine this?

Answer:
Unless the infant was suffocated immediately when it was born, the first breath that it took would start to inflate the lungs and some of the air would be trapped in the lungs. By placing the lungs in water to see if they would float or not, the medical examiner can determine whether or not there is any air in the lungs. Other measurements and tests could also be used to determine if the infant had breathed at all (air in the lungs) or was dead at birth (lungs collapsed with a small amount of fluid).

Chapter 17:   The Digestive System

Multiple Choice

1. Each of the following organs is a component of the digestive tract
   except one. Identify the exception.
   a. stomach
   b. pharynx
   c. esophagus
   d. spleen
   e. colon

   Answer: d

2. Which of the following is an accessory organ of digestion?
   a. stomach
   b. pancreas
   c. spleen
   d. colon
   e. esophagus

   Answer: b

3. Digestion refers to
   a. the progressive dehydration of indigestible residue
   b. the input of food into the digestive tract
   c. the chemical breakdown of food
   d. the absorption of nutrients in the gut
   e. the mixing of nutrients with digestive enzymes

   Answer: c

4. Which of the following is not a digestive function?
   a. mechanical processing
   b. absorption
   c. compaction
   d. ingestion
   e. filtration

   Answer: e

5. The mucous epithelium is a component of the
   a. serosa
   b. muscularis
   c. submucosa
   d. mucosa
   e. adventia

   Answer: d

6. Contraction of the _____ layer of the intestinal wall functions to change the shape of the intestinal lumen and moves food through its length.
   a. mucosa
   b. submucosa
   c. serosa
   d. muscularis
   e. adventitia

Answer: d

7. The _____ are double sheets of peritoneal membrane that hold some of the visceral organs in their proper position.
   a. serosa
   b. adventitia
   c. mesenteries
   d. fibrosa
   e. muscularis

Answer: c

8. Large blood vessels and lymphatics are found in the
   a. mucosa
   b. submucosa
   c. muscularis
   d. adventitia
   e. serosa

Answer: b

9. Most of the digestive tract is lined by
   a. pseudostratified ciliated columnar epithelium
   b. cuboidal epithelium
   c. stratified squamous epithelium
   d. simple epithelium
   e. simple columnar epithelium

Answer: e

10. A stratified squamous epithelial lining can be found in the
    a. rectum
    b. esophagus
    c. oral cavity
    d. oropharynx
    e. all of the above

Answer: e

11. A modification of the mucosa of the small intestines that allows for expansion of the organ are the
    a. flat surfaces
    b. mucus glands
    c. ciliated columnar cells
    d. plicae
    e. muscularis smooth muscle

    Answer: d

12. In smooth muscle,
    a. there are no striations
    b. myofilaments are present
    c. there are no sarcomeres
    d. contractions cause the cell to twist like a corkscrew
    e. all of the above

    Answer: e

13. In visceral smooth muscle,
    a. the cells are linearly arranged as long fibers
    b. adjacent cells are connected by synapses
    c. when one muscle cell contracts, the contraction spreads as a wave through the whole tissue
    d. contraction can only be stimulated by neurotransmitters
    e. all of the above

    Answer: c

14. Waves of muscular contractions that propel the contents of the digestive tract from one point to another are called
    a. segmentations
    b. pendulum movements
    c. peristalsis
    d. churning movements
    e. mastications

    Answer: c

15. Regional movements that occur in the small intestine and function to churn and fragment the digestive materials are called
    a. segmentation
    b. pendulum movements
    c. peristalsis
    d. churning movements
    e. mastication

    Answer: a

16. The functions of the oral cavity include
    a. analysis of material before swallowing and partial digestion of proteins and carbohydrates
    b. mechanical processing of food
    c. lubrication
    d. b and c only
    e. all of the above

    Answer: d

17. _____ pair(s) of salivary glands secrete into the oral cavity.
    a. 1
    b. 2
    c. 3
    d. 4
    e. 5

    Answer: c

18. The _____ gland empties into the upper regions of the oral cavity.
    a. submaxillary
    b. submandibular
    c. parotid
    d. sublingual
    e. vestibular

    Answer: c

19. Functions of the tongue include
    a. mechanical processing of food
    b. manipulation of food
    c. sensory analysis of food
    d. a and b only
    e. all of the above

    Answer: e

20. Teeth are similar to bone and contain a mineralized matrix called
    a. enamel
    b. cementum
    c. dentin
    d. pulp
    e. periodontium

    Answer: c

21. The portion of a tooth containing blood vessels and nerves is the
    a. enamel
    b. cementum
    c. dentin
    d. pulp
    e. periodontium

Answer: d

22. The root of a tooth is covered by
    a. enamel
    b. cementum
    c. dentin
    d. pulp
    e. the root canal

Answer: b

23. The crown of a tooth is covered by
    a. enamel
    b. cementum
    c. dentin
    d. pulp
    e. periodontium

Answer: a

24. During swallowing,
    a. the soft palate elevates
    b. the larynx elevates
    c. the epiglottis closes
    d. the upper esophageal sphincter opens
    e. all of the above

Answer: e

25. Secretions from the salivary glands
    a. are mostly digestive enzymes
    b. help to control bacterial populations in the mouth
    c. help to lubricate the oral cavity and its contents
    d. b and c only
    e. all of the above

Answer: d

26. The lateral walls of the oral cavity are formed by the
    a. vestibule
    b. cheeks
    c. gingiva
    d. tongue
    e. pharynx

    Answer: b

27. The space between the tongue and the teeth is called the
    a. pharynx
    b. larynx
    c. epiglottis
    d. vestibule
    e. cheek

    Answer: d

28. The uvula is located at the
    a. posterior of the tongue
    b. margin of the vestibule
    c. base of the lower teeth
    d. posterior margin of the soft palate
    e. margin of the oropharynx and the laryngopharynx

    Answer: d

29. The _____ are blade-shaped teeth that function in cutting or chopping.
    a. wisdom teeth
    b. incisors
    c. bicuspids
    d. cuspids
    e. molars

    Answer: b

30. The _____ are pointed teeth that are adapted for tearing and shredding.
    a. incisors
    b. bicuspids
    c. wisdom teeth
    d. cuspids
    e. molars

    Answer: a

31. The _____ are teeth with flattened crowns and prominent ridges that are adapted for grinding.
    a. molars
    b. cuspids
    c. eye teeth
    d. canines
    e. bicuspids

    Answer: a

32. The esophagus
    a. extends from the oropharynx to the stomach
    b. is a muscular tube
    c. functions in digestion of carbohydrates
    d. has a thick lining that will tolerate stomach acid
    e. all of the above

    Answer: b

33. Functions of the stomach include
    a. storage of recently ingested food
    b. mechanical breakdown of food
    c. denaturation of proteins
    d. initiation of protein digestion
    e. all of the above

    Answer: e

34. Parietal cells secrete
    a. pepsin
    b. gastrin
    c. mucus
    d. hydrochloric acid
    e. all of the above

    Answer: d

35. Chief cells secrete
    a. pepsinogen
    b. gastrin
    c. mucus
    d. hydrochloric acid
    e. intrinsic factor

    Answer: a

36. The portion of the stomach that connects to the esophagus is the
    a. fundus
    b. cardia
    c. body
    d. antrum
    e. pylorus

    Answer: b

37. The bulge of the greater curvature of the stomach superior to the esophageal junction is the
    a. cardia
    b. pylorus
    c. fundus
    d. antrum
    e. body

    Answer: c

38. The large area of the stomach between the fundus and the J-curve is the
    a. body
    b. antrum
    c. pylorus
    d. cardia
    e. fundus

    Answer: a

39. The curved, tubular portion of the stomach is the
    a. antrum
    b. fundus
    c. body
    d. cardia
    e. pylorus

    Answer: e

40. The prominent ridges in the lining of the stomach are called
    a. papillae
    b. cardia
    c. rugae
    d. plicae
    e. valvulae

    Answer: c

41. The greater omentum is
    a. a major portion of the stomach
    b. attached to the stomach at the lesser curvature
    c. important in the digestion of fats
    d. a fatty sheet that hangs like an apron over the abdominal viscera
    e. a sheet of connective tissue that attaches the stomach to the liver and pancreas

    Answer: d

42. Gastric pits are
    a. ridges in the body of the stomach
    b. involved in absorption of liquids from the stomach
    c. pockets in the lining of the stomach that contain secretory cells
    d. located in the esophagus
    e. areas where proteins are digested

    Answer: c

43. The enzyme pepsin digests
    a. carbohydrates
    b. proteins
    c. lipids
    d. nucleic acids
    e. vitamins

    Answer: b

44. Lacteals
    a. increase the surface area of the mucosa of the small intestine
    b. carry products of digestion that will not pass through the walls of blood capillaries
    c. produce new cells for the mucosa of the small intestine
    d. secrete digestive enzymes
    e. produce hormones

    Answer: b

45. Plicae and intestinal villi
    a. increase the surface area of the mucosa of the small intestine
    b. carry products of digestion that will not pass through the walls of blood capillaries
    c. produce new cells for the mucosa of the small intestine
    d. secrete digestive enzymes
    e. produce hormones

    Answer: a

46. Intestinal glands
    a. increase the surface area of the mucosa of the small intestine
    b. carry products of digestion that will not pass through the walls of blood capillaries
    c. produce new cells for the mucosa of the small intestine
    d. function in the absorption of nutrients
    e. secrete a watery intestinal juice

    Answer: e

47. Absorptive effectiveness of the small intestine is enhanced by
    a. plicae
    b. villi
    c. microvilli
    d. intestinal movements
    e. all of the above

    Answer: e

48. The most striking aspect of intestinal histology is
    a. the large number of mucus-producing goblet cells
    b. the complexity of the enzyme-secreting cells
    c. the large number of endocrine cells
    d. the adaptation for increasing absorptive area
    e. the variety of the cells lining the mucosa

    Answer: d

49. The portion of the small intestine that is attached to the pylorus of the stomach is the
    a. ileum
    b. colon
    c. cecum
    d. jejunum
    e. duodenum

    Answer: e

50. The middle portion of the small intestine is the
    a. ileum
    b. duodenum
    c. jejunum
    d. pylorus
    e. cecum

    Answer: c

51. The portion of the small intestine that attaches to the large intestine is the
    a. cecum
    b. appendix
    c. ileum
    d. jejunum
    e. duodenum

Answer: c

52. Plicae are
    a. ridges in the wall of the stomach
    b. transverse folds in the mucosa of the small intestine
    c. finger-like projections on the surface of the mucosa of the small intestine
    d. sacculations in the colon
    e. abnormal structures formed by excessive pressure in the small intestine

Answer: b

53. An intestinal hormone that stimulates the pancreas to release a watery secretion that is high in bicarbonate ion is
    a. enterocrinin
    b. secretin
    c. cholecystokinin
    d. GIP
    e. gastrin

Answer: b

54. An intestinal hormone that stimulates the gall bladder to release bile is
    a. enterokinase
    b. secretin
    c. cholecystokinin
    d. GIP
    e. gastrin

Answer: c

55. An intestinal hormone that stimulates the release of insulin from the pancreatic islet cells is
    a. enterocrinin
    b. enterokinase
    c. secretin
    d. cholecystokinin
    e. GIP

Answer: e

56. An intestinal hormone that stimulates parietal cells and chief cells in the stomach to secrete is
    a. secretin
    b. enterokinase
    c. cholecystokinin
    d. gastrin
    e. GIP

    Answer: d

57. The human liver is composed of _____ lobe(s).
    a. 1
    b. 2
    c. 3
    d. 4
    e. 5

    Answer: d

58. The fusion of the hepatic duct with the cystic duct forms
    a. the hepatic portal vein
    b. the porta hepatis
    c. the common bile duct
    d. the common pancreatic duct
    e. the bile canaliculus

    Answer: c

59. In the center of a liver lobule there is a
    a. hepatic duct
    b. portal area
    c. capillary bed
    d. central vein
    e. portal vein

    Answer: d

60. The exocrine portion of the pancreas is composed of
    a. islets of Langerhans
    b. pancreatic crypts
    c. pancreatic acini
    d. pancreatic lobules
    e. triads

    Answer: c

61. Each of the following is a function of the liver **except** one. Identify the exception.
    a. synthesis and secretion of bile
    b. antibody production
    c. synthesis of plasma proteins
    d. inactivation of toxins
    e. storage of glycogen and lipids

    Answer: b

62. The basic functional units of the liver are the
    a. hepatocytes
    b. liver cells
    c. lobules
    d. portal areas
    e. bile canaliculi

    Answer: c

63. _____ are arranged within a lobule of the liver into a series of plates radiating outward from a central vein.
    a. Portal cells
    b. Hepatocytes
    c. Bile canaliculi
    d. Bile ducts
    e. Hepatic ducts

    Answer: b

64. The pancreas produces
    a. lipases
    b. amylase
    c. proteinases
    d. carbohydrases
    e. all of the above

    Answer: e

65. Bile is stored in the
    a. liver
    b. duodenum
    c. pancreas
    d. gall bladder
    e. appendix

    Answer: d

66. Functions of the large intestine include
    a. chemical digestion of chyme
    b. temporary food storage
    c. resorption of water and compaction of feces
    d. absorption of the products of digestion
    e. all of the above

    Answer: c

67. At the hepatic flexure, the colon becomes the
    a. ascending colon
    b. transverse colon
    c. descending colon
    d. sigmoid colon
    e. rectum

    Answer: b

68. The last approximate 15 cm of the digestive tract is the
    a. anus
    b. anal canal
    c. rectum
    d. sigmoid colon
    e. rectal column

    Answer: c

69. Haustrae are
    a. external pouches of the colon
    b. ridges in the mucosa of the colon
    c. glands in the large intestine that secrete enzymes
    d. the source of hormones produced by the colon
    e. feces stored in the rectum

    Answer: a

70. The taenia coli are
    a. external pouches of the colon
    b. three longitudinal bands of muscle located beneath the serosa of the colon
    c. ridges in the mucosa of the colon
    d. polyps that obstruct the sigmoid colon
    e. tumors normally found in the ascending colon

    Answer: b

71. An expandable pouch in the region of the ileum at the ileocecal valve is the
    a. appendix
    b. sigmoid colon
    c. rectum
    d. haustra
    e. cecum

    Answer: e

72. A small, finger-like structure attached to the "blind" end of the cecum is the
    a. haustra
    b. pancreas
    c. gall bladder
    d. appendix
    e. ileum

    Answer: d

73. The enzyme amylase helps to digest
    a. proteins
    b. complex carbohydrates
    c. simple sugars
    d. lipids
    e. nucleic acids

    Answer: b

74. An enzyme that will digest proteins into polypeptides is
    a. lipase
    b. amylase
    c. nuclease
    d. maltase
    e. trypsin

    Answer: e

75. Carbohydrate digestion begins in the
    a. mouth
    b. esophagus
    c. stomach
    d. duodenum
    e. ileum

    Answer: a

76. Most products of fat digestion are absorbed
    a. by capillaries
    b. by veins
    c. by lymphatic vessels
    d. by the arterioles
    e. by the interstitial fluid

    Answer: c

77. Which of the following changes in the digestive system occur with advancing age?
    a. a decrease in smooth tone
    b. weaker peristaltic contractions
    c. a thinner epithelial lining
    d. a reduction in epithelial stem cell division
    e. all of the above

    Answer: e

78. During the cephalic phase of gastric secretion
    a. the stomach responds to distention
    b. secretin inhibits parietal and chief cells
    c. there is an increased flow of action potentials along the vagus nerve to the stomach
    d. the intestine reflex inhibits gastric emptying
    e. production of gastric juice slows down

    Answer: c

79. The gastric phase of gastric secretion is triggered by
    a. the sight, thought or smell of food
    b. the entry of food into the stomach
    c. the entry of chyme into the small intestine
    d. the entry of chyme into the large intestine
    e. the release of cholecystokinin and secretin by the small intestine

    Answer: b

80. The intestinal phase of gastric activity
    a. begins when chyme enters the small intestine
    b. functions to control the rate of gastric emptying
    c. involves both neural and endocrine reflexes
    d. helps to ensure that the functions of the small intestine proceed with relative efficiency
    e. all of the above

    Answer: e

81. Decreased levels of bile salts in the bile would interfere with
    a. protein digestion
    b. fat digestion
    c. digestion of disaccharides
    d. digestion of complex carbohydrates
    e. digestion of vitamins

    Answer: b

82. The lining of the stomach
    a. is composed of simple columnar epithelium
    b. is covered by a thick, viscous mucus
    c. is constantly being replaced
    d. contains gastric pits
    e. all of the above

    Answer: e

83. Which of the following is greater?
    a. the pH of the blood in gastric veins during digestion of a large meal
    b. the pH of the blood in gastric veins following a 24-hour fast

    Answer: a

84. In response to the arrival of acid chyme in the duodenum, the
    a. blood levels of secretin rise
    b. blood levels of cholecystokinin fall
    c. blood levels of gastrin rise
    d. blood levels of enterocrinin fall
    e. all of the above

    Answer: a

85. Which of the following is faster?
    a. the normal rate of peristalsis in the small intestine
    b. the normal rate of peristalsis in the colon

    Answer: a

86. A blockage of the ducts from the parotid glands would
    a. result in the production of more viscous saliva
    b. impair the lubricating properties of saliva
    c. interfere with carbohydrate digestion in the mouth
    d. eliminate the sense of taste
    e. all of the above

    Answer: c

87. Increased parasympathetic stimulation of the intestine would result in
    a. decreased motility
    b. decreased secretion
    c. decreased sensitivity of local reflexes
    d. decreased segmentation
    e. none of the above

    Answer: e

88. During defecation
    a. stretch receptors in the rectal wall initiate a series of peristaltic contractions in the colon and rectum
    b. stretch receptors in the rectal wall activate parasympathetic centers in the sacral region of the spinal cord
    c. the internal anal sphincter relaxes
    d. the external anal sphincter is consciously relaxed
    e. all of the above

    Answer: e

89. A drug that blocks the action of the hormone cholecystokinin would affect
    a. the amount of bile produced by the liver
    b. the composition of pancreatic secretions
    c. the level of intestinal gastrin
    d. secretions of the duodenal glands
    e. all of the above

    Answer: b

90. An obstruction of the cystic duct would result in
    a. pancreatitis
    b. jaundice
    c. inability to digest protein
    d. increased sugar in the chyme
    e. an inability to absorb water-soluble vitamins

    Answer: b

91. Tom is suffering from hepatitis, an inflammation of the liver. Which of the following symptoms would you expect to observe in Tom?
    a. jaundice
    b. elevated levels of blood glucose
    c. impaired digestion of protein
    d. blood in the feces
    e. all of the above

    Answer: a

92. Functions of the oral cavity include all of the following **except**:
    a. digesting proteins
    b. analyzing materials before swallowing
    c. lubricating materials by mixing them with mucus
    d. digesting carbohydrates
    e. altering the size of food particles

    Answer: a

93. Teeth used to bite off the tips of food are the
    a. cuspids
    b. bicuspids
    c. canines
    d. molars
    e. incisors

    Answer: e

94. Of the following, which is not a function of saliva?
    a. breaking down complex carbohydrates
    b. forming a bolus for ease in swallowing
    c. digesting proteins
    d. cleaning teeth
    e. altering the pH of the mouth

    Answer: c

95. The salivary glands that produce secretions rich in salivary amylase are the
    a. sublingual glands
    b. submandibular glands
    c. lingual glands
    d. parotid glands
    e. submaxillary glands

    Answer: d

96. The cells responsible for the secretion of pepsinogen are called
    a. parietal cells
    b. chief cells
    c. cephalic cells
    d. gastric cells
    e. none of the above

    Answer: b

97. Trypsin is an enzyme that breaks down
    a. carbohydrates
    b. lipids
    c. proteins
    d. minerals
    e. vitamins

    Answer: c

98. Gastrin is released in response to
    a. proteins, alcohol, and caffeine
    b. parasympathetic innervation
    c. the sight of food
    d. the smell of food
    e. chyme entering the esophagus

    Answer: a

99. Persons who have undergone a total gastrectomy can survive because the stomach's only absolutely vital function is
    a. absorption of nutrients
    b. secretion of amylase
    c. secretion of intrinsic factor
    d. digestion of proteins
    e. water absorption

    Answer: c

100. Pancreatic secretions range in pH from
    a. 1.2 - 3.5
    b. 4.0 - 5.0
    c. 6.0 - 7.0
    d. 7.5 - 8.8
    e. 8.9 - 10.0

    Answer: d

101. Bile salts are responsible for the digestion and absorption of
    a. fats
    b. proteins
    c. carbohydrates
    d. minerals
    e. vitamins

    Answer: a

102. Major regions of the <u>large intestine</u> include the
     a. cecum, colon, duodenum
     b. duodenum, ileum, jejunum
     c. cecum, colon, duodenum
     d. ascending colon, descending colon, ileum
     e. cecum, colon, rectum

     Answer: e

103. Regions of the colon include the
     a. ascending colon, transverse colon, descending colon, and sigmoid colon
     b. cecum, bowel, duodenum, and jejunum
     c. transverse colon, rectum, duodenum, and jejunum
     d. ascending colon, duodenum, jejunum, and ileum
     e. cecum, descending colon, sigmoid colon, and duodenum

     Answer: a

104. Regions of the <u>small intestine</u> include all of the following **except**:
     a. duodenum
     b. cecum
     c. jejunum
     d. ileum
     e. all are correct

     Answer: b

105. Nutrients generally absorbed by the large intestine are
     a. electrolytes
     b. water
     c. fats
     d. proteins
     e. a and b are correct

     Answer: e

106. The four regions of the stomach include all of the following **except**:
     a. cardiac
     b. gastric
     c. fundic
     d. body
     e. pyloric

     Answer: b

Matching

107. Match the description in the first column with the term in the second column

     _____1. extends from dentin of tooth root to bone
     _____2. structure hanging from the pharyngeal arch
     _____3. enzyme that breaks down starch
     _____4. structure that anchors the tongue to the mouth floor
     _____5. roof of the oral cavity

A. uvula
B. frenulum
C. palate
D. amylase
E. periodontal ligament

Answer: 1-e, 2-a, 3-d, 4-b, 5-c

Fill-In-The-Blank

108. The compound necessary for the absorption of vitamin B12 is called _____ _____.

Answer: intrinsic factor

109. _____ ulcers result from the excessive production of acid or the inadequate production of the alkaline mucus that poses an epithelial defense.

Answer: Peptic

110. The _____ ligament marks the division between the left and right lobes of the liver.

Answer: falciform

111. The oral cavity is also known as the _____ cavity.

Answer: buccal

112. The first set of teeth to appear are the _____ teeth.

Answer: deciduous

113. There are normally a total of _____ primary teeth.

Answer: 20

114. The secondary dentition usually contains _____ teeth.

Answer: 32

115. The proper term for chewing is _____.

Answer: mastication

116. A small, semi-solid mass of food that is the result of proper mastication is called a(n) _____.

Answer: bolus

117. After processing in the stomach, the gastric contents are referred to as _____.

Answer: chyme

118. Bile salts aid in the digestion of fats by _____ large fat droplets.

Answer: emulsifying

119. The enzyme that digests starch into disaccharides and monosaccharides is _____.

Answer: amylase

Essay

120. Dave is under a lot of stress at his job and at home. He begins to feel discomfort and a burning sensation in his abdomen following a meal. After consulting a doctor, he finds that he has developed a duodenal ulcer. he does not understand how being nervous would cause the ulcer and asks you to explain. What would you tell Dave?

Answer:
The body's normal response to stress is increased sympathoadrenal activity. Increased stimulation of the digestive tract by the sympathetic nerves would cause a decrease in mucus secretion in the small intestine as well as decreased motility. After a meal, the acid chyme would not be neutralized as efficiently because of the decreased mucus, and the irritating action would remain longer because of the decreased motility. In addition, bile that may enter from the liver has a detergent action that would further remove the mucus protection from the cells making them more vulnerable to the effects of the stomach acid.

121. How would you describe the condition known as lactose intolerance to another individual who believes she may be suffering from this because she experiences gastric distress after consuming dairy products?

Answer:
An adult deficiency in lactose can lead to lactose intolerance. The cause of this appears to be genetic. Lactase works in the small intestine as a catalyst that aids in the hydrolysis of the disaccharide lactose, which is common in milk-based products. The inability to digest lactose into its monosaccharides leads to the fermentation of the molecule by intestinal bacteria into unpleasant products such as gases and acids. Treatments of this disease include ingesting commercial products that supply the missing enzyme, such as acidophilus milk and Lactate drops or tablets.

Chapter 18:   Nutrition and Metabolism

Multiple Choice

1. The sum of all of the biochemical processes going on within the human body at any given instant is called
   a. glycolysis
   b. oxidation
   c. catabolism
   d. anabolism
   e. metabolism

   Answer: e

2. Cells synthesize new organic components
   a. to perform structural maintenance
   b. to perform repairs
   c. to support growth
   d. b and c only
   e. all of the above

   Answer: e

3. During glycolysis
   a. a molecule of glucose is converted into two molecules of pyruvic acid
   b. 6 molecules of ATP are produced
   c. carbon dioxide is produced
   d. NADH2 molecules attach to the cytochromes
   e. more energy is used than is released

   Answer: a

4. Inside of the mitochondrion, during the transition reaction, each pyruvic acid molecule
   a. forms a molecule of citric acid
   b. loses a carbon atom
   c. attaches to NAD
   d. directly enters the electron transport system
   e. has a phosphate ion added to it

   Answer: b

5. The TCA cycle
   a. begins with the formation of a molecule of citric acid
   b. directly produces most of the ATP from the catabolism of glucose
   c. does not form any carbon dioxide
   d. contains enzymes called cytochromes
   e. forms acetyl-CoA from glucose

   Answer: a

6. The carbon dioxide of respiration is formed during
   a. glycolysis
   b. the TCA cycle
   c. electron transport
   d. the formation of pyruvic acid
   e. the formation of water

Answer: b

7. The TCA cycle must turn ___ times to completely metabolize the pyruvic acid produced from one glucose molecule.
   a. 1
   b. 2
   c. 3
   d. 4
   e. 5

Answer: b

8. In glycolysis, each molecule of glucose metabolized releases enough energy to form ___ molecules of ATP.
   a. 2
   b. 4
   c. 30
   d. 36
   e. 38

Answer: a

9. In the process of cellular respiration, each molecule of glucose that is metabolized releases enough energy to form ___ molecules of ATP.
   a. 2
   b. 4
   c. 30
   d. 36
   e. 38

Answer: d

10. During lipolysis
    a. triglycerides are converted into molecules of acetyl-CoA
    b. triglycerides are broken down into glycerol and fatty acids
    c. lipids are converted into glucose molecules
    d. lipids are formed from excess carbohydrates
    e. lipids are metabolized to yield ATP

Answer: b

11. Beta-oxidation
    a. occurs in the mitochondria
    b. is the process that breaks down fatty acids into two-carbon fragments that can be metabolized by the TCA cycle
    c. yields large amounts of ATP, while requiring coenzyme A, NAD, and FAD
    d. a and b only
    e. none of the above

    Answer: e

12. Lipids
    a. release less energy than an equivalent amount of glucose
    b. are difficult to store since they are not water soluble
    c. are easily mobilized from their reserves
    d. release more energy than an equivalent amount of glucose
    e. all of the above

    Answer: d

13. Lipogenesis generally begins with
    a. glucose
    b. amino acids
    c. fatty acids
    d. acetyl Co-A
    e. succinyl Co-A

    Answer: d

14. The largest metabolic reserves for the average adult are stored as
    a. carbohydrates
    b. proteins
    c. amino acids
    d. triglycerides
    e. fatty acids

    Answer: d

15. Lipoproteins that deliver cholesterol to peripheral tissues are called:
    a. low density lipoproteins (LDLs)
    b. high density lipoproteins (HDLs)

    Answer: a

16. Lipoproteins that carry mostly cholesterol and phospholipids from peripheral tissues to the liver are called
    a. low density lipoproteins (LDLs)
    b. high density lipoproteins (HDLs)

    Answer: b

17. In transamination, the amino group of an amino acid is
    a. converted to ammonia
    b. converted to urea
    c. transferred to another carbon chain
    d. transferred to a molecule in the glycolytic pathway
    e. transferred to acetyl-Co-A

    Answer: c

18. Urea is formed in the
    a. liver
    b. stomach
    c. kidneys
    d. small intestine
    e. large intestine

    Answer: a

19. The process of deamination produces
    a. keto acids
    b. urea
    c. ammonia
    d. acetyl-Co-A
    e. B vitamins

    Answer: c

20. Nucleotides from RNA
    a. are deaminated to form ammonia
    b. can provide sugars for glycolysis
    c. can be used to synthesize proteins
    d. cannot be used as a source of energy for the production of ATP
    e. cannot be recycled

    Answer: b

21. A balanced diet should
    a. include adequate substrates for the production of energy
    b. provide essential amino acids
    c. provide essential fatty acids
    d. contain adequate amounts of vitamins and minerals
    e. all of the above

    Answer: e

22. Nitrogen compounds of the body include
    a. amino acids
    b. nucleotides
    c. creatine
    d. porphyrins
    e. all of the above

    Answer: e

23. The nutrients that yield the most energy per gram when metabolized are
    a. carbohydrates
    b. proteins
    c. fats
    d. nucleic acids
    e. vitamins

    Answer: c

24. The major anion in body fluids is
    a. chloride ion
    b. bicarbonate ion
    c. sulfate ion
    d. iodide ion

    Answer: a

25. A cation that is essential for muscle contraction, nerve function, and blood clotting is
    a. sodium
    b. potassium
    c. calcium
    d. magnesium
    e. selenium

    Answer: c

26. An ion that is a necessary component of high-energy compounds and nucleic acids, and a structural component of bone is
    a. chloride ion
    b. sulfate ion
    c. phosphate ion
    d. bicarbonate ion
    e. iodide ion

    Answer: c

27. A mineral that is a component of hemoglobin, myoglobin, and cytochromes is
    a. calcium
    b. magnesium
    c. iron
    d. zinc
    e. cobalt

Answer: c

28. A mineral that is a necessary cofactor for hemoglobin synthesis is
    a. zinc
    b. copper
    c. cobalt
    d. iodine
    e. silicon

Answer: b

29. The vitamin that is required for the synthesis of visual pigments is
    a. vitamin A
    b. vitamin B
    c. vitamin C
    d. vitamin D
    e. vitamin E

Answer: a

30. The vitamin that is required for proper bone growth and for calcium absorption and retention is
    a. vitamin A
    b. vitamin B
    c. vitamin C
    d. vitamin D
    e. vitamin E

Answer: d

31. The vitamin that is essential for the production of several clotting factors is
    a. vitamin A
    b. vitamin B
    c. vitamin E
    d. vitamin C
    e. vitamin K

Answer: e

32. The vitamin that is a constituent of the coenzymes FAD and FMN is
    a. thiamine
    b. riboflavin
    c. niacin
    d. folacin
    e. cobalamin

    Answer: b

33. The vitamin that is a constituent of the coenzyme NAD is
    a. thiamine
    b. riboflavin
    c. niacin
    d. folacin
    e. cobalamin

    Answer: c

34. The vitamin that plays the role of a coenzyme in amino acid and lipid metabolism is
    a. vitamin B6
    b. pantothenic acid
    c. riboflavin
    d. folacin
    e. niacin

    Answer: a

35. The vitamin that is a coenzyme in amino acid and nucleic acid metabolism is
    a. pantothenic acid
    b. vitamin B6
    c. folacin
    d. vitamin C
    e. vitamin K

    Answer: c

36. The food group that yields the most energy per gram when metabolized is
    a. vitamins
    b. carbohydrates
    c. fats
    d. proteins
    e. nucleic acids

    Answer: c

37. Factors that influence an individual's BMR (basal metabolic rate) include
    a. sex
    b. age
    c. body weight
    d. genetics
    e. all of the above

    Answer: e

38. Which of the following is not an effect when body temperature rises?
    a. Peripheral blood vessels dilate.
    b. Secretion from sweat glands increases.
    c. Depth of respiration decreases.
    d. Heat is lost through radiation from the skin.
    e. All of the above are true effects.

    Answer: c

39. The primary function of the TCA cycle in carbohydrate metabolism is to
    a. produce 30 ATPs
    b. produce carbon dioxide
    c. produce oxygen
    d. supply electrons to coenzymes NAD and FAD
    e. form GTP, another high energy phosphate-bond molecule

    Answer: d

40. The major steps in the electron transport chain include
    a. removal of hydrogen atoms from a substrate molecule by coenzymes
    b. ionization of hydrogen atoms
    c. increasing the energy level of electrons passing through the electron transport chain
    d. the loss of electrons by oxygen atoms
    e. all of the above

    Answer: a

41. In the electron transport chain, energy for the synthesis of ATP is provided by
    a. the splitting of oxygen molecules
    b. the breaking of the covalent bonds in glucose
    c. the movement of hydrogen ions through channels in the respiratory enzymes
    d. the combination of two atoms of hydrogen and one atom of oxygen to form water
    e. the oxidation of acetyl-CoA

    Answer: c

42. Inadequate exposure to sunlight could result in decreased amounts of vitamin _____ in the body.
    a. A
    b. B12
    c. C
    d. D
    e. E

Answer: d

43. Impaired fat absorption in the intestine would interfere with the absorption of vitamin
    a. A
    b. B12
    c. C
    d. niacin
    e. riboflavin

Answer: a

44. Which of the following individuals would have the greater BMR?
    a. a 34-year-old nursing mother
    b. a 34-year-old non-pregnant, non-nursing woman

Answer: a

45. Two individuals are the same age, sex, and ethnic background. While being tested for their BMRs, Bill consumes 20 liters of oxygen/hour and Randy consumes 16 liters of oxygen/hour. Which of the two needs to consume the most calories in order to maintain proper health and constant weight?
    a. Bill
    b. Randy

Answer: a

46. Which of the following individuals would lose heat faster in a cold room?
    a. an adult man
    b. an adult woman
    c. an adolescent male
    d. a child
    e. a newborn infant

Answer: e

47. Which of the following would lose heat faster
    a. an obese person
    b. a tall thin person

Answer: b

48. If you were in a desert without water, which nutrient would you like to have stored in your body in a large amount?
    a. protein
    b. sugars
    c. complex carbohydrates
    d. fat
    e. amino acids

    Answer: d

49. On a tour of African countries, Don contracts a bad case of traveler's diarrhea. Because he cannot eat very much, his body starts to use energy sources other than carbohydrates. This would result in
    a. increased levels of urea in the blood
    b. ketosis
    c. a decreased blood pH
    d. increased gluconeogenesis in the liver
    e. all of the above

    Answer: e

50. Identify the false statement from the ones listed below.
    a. The cholesterol content of the diet is not the only source for circulating cholesterol.
    b. Genetic factors affect each individual's cholesterol level.
    c. Cholesterol levels remain relatively stable throughout life.
    d. Cholesterol has many vital functions in humans.
    e. At age 19, females tend to have slightly higher cholesterol levels than their male counterparts.

    Answer: c

51. In the condition ketoacidosis,
    a. pH may drop below 7.05
    b. cardiac arrhythmias occur
    c. coma could result
    d. death could be a consequence
    e. all of the above

    Answer: e

52. Diets containing too many calories and too many lipids by proportion increase the incidence of:
    a. obesity
    b. heart disease and atherosclerosis
    c. diabetes
    d. hypertension
    e. all of the above

    Answer: e

53. A mineral necessary for normal membrane function is:
   a. calcium
   b. potassium
   c. manganese
   d. zinc
   e. iron

   Answer: b

54. This mineral is a cofactor of the carbonic anhydrase enzyme system.
   a. chloride
   b. calcium
   c. copper
   d. zinc
   e. magnesium

   Answer: d

55. The fat-soluble vitamins include:
   a. A, D, E, and K
   b. A, B, C, and D
   c. B, biotin, C and A
   d. niacin, B, folacin, and biotin
   e. C, biotin, A, and K

   Answer: a

56. Minerals do all of the following **except**:
   a. serve as cofactors
   b. contribute to the osmolarity of body fluids
   c. provide energy
   d. play a role in membrane potentials
   e. are important to gas transport

   Answer: c

57. The only natural dietary source(s) for vitamin B12 are
   a. milk
   b. meat
   c. vegetables
   d. A and B
   e. citrus fruits

   Answer: d

Fill-In-The-Blank

58. Those nutrients that the body cannot synthesize or cannot synthesize in adequate amounts are termed _____.

   Answer: essential

59. In order for vitamin B12 to be absorbed, it must be bound to _____ _____, which is secreted by the gastric mucosa.

    Answer: intrinsic factor

60. The process of synthesizing glucose from lipids, amino acids, or other carbohydrates is called _____.

    Answer: gluconeogenesis

61. _____ are lipoproteins that are formed in the intestine to carry lipids into circulation.

    Answer: Chylomicrons

62. Lipoproteins that contain large amounts of cholesterol that are being transported in peripheral tissues are called _____.

    Answer: low-density lipoproteins (LDLs)

63. The nucleic acid that can be metabolized to supply energy is _____.

    Answer: RNA

64. _____ is an unhealthy state resulting from inadequate intake of one or more nutrients that becomes life-threatening as the deficiencies accumulate.

    Answer: Malnutrition

65. A(n) _____ _____ contains all of the ingredients necessary to maintain homeostasis.

    Answer: balanced diet

66. A complete _____ contains all of the essential amino acids.

    Answer: protein

67. A(n) _____ _____ is deficient in one or more of the essential amino acids.

    Answer: incomplete protein

68. _____ are inorganic ions released through the dissociation of electrolytes.

    Answer: Minerals

69. The unit of measurement used for the energy content of food is the
_____.

    Answer: calorie or kilocalorie

70. The _____ _____ _____ represents the minimum resting
energy expenditures of an awake, alert individual.

    Answer: basal metabolic rate or BMR

71. _____ is the homeostatic process that allows us to maintain a
constant body temperature.

    Answer: Thermoregulation

72. _____ is the loss of heat energy by vaporizing water.

    Answer: Evaporation

Essay

73. Charlie has a blood test that shows a normal level of LDLs but an
elevated level of HDLs in his blood. Since his family has a history of
cardiovascular disease, he wonders if he should modify his lifestyle.
What would you tell him?

    Answer:
    Based just on the information given, Charlie would appear to be in good
    health, at least relative to his diet and probable exercise. Problems
    are associated with elevated levels of LDLs which carry cholesterol to
    peripheral tissues and make it available for the formation of
    atherosclerotic plaques in blood vessels. High levels of HDLs indicate
    that a considerable amount of cholesterol is being removed from the
    peripheral tissues and carried to the liver for disposal. You would
    encourage Charlie not to change, and keep up the good work.

Chapter 19:   The Urinary System

Multiple Choice

1. The urinary system
   a. regulates plasma concentrations of electrolytes
   b. regulates blood volume by removing RBCs from circulation
   c. contributes to stabilizing blood pH
   d. a and c only
   e. all of the above

   Answer: d

2. Urine is produced by the
   a. liver
   b. urinary bladder
   c. kidney
   d. ureter
   e. urethra

   Answer: c

3. Urine is carried to the urinary bladder by
   a. blood vessels
   b. lymphatics
   c. the ureters
   d. the urethra
   e. all of the above

   Answer: c

4. Each of the following organs is part of the urinary system **except** one.
   Identify the exception.
   a. kidney
   b. urinary bladder
   c. liver
   d. ureter
   e. urethra

   Answer: c

5. The kidneys
   a. are located in a position that is retroperitoneal
   b. are surrounded by a renal capsule
   c. are protected by the lower ribs of the rib cage
   d. a and b only
   e. all of the above

   Answer: d

6. The prominent indentation on the medial surface of the kidney is the
   a. calyx
   b. pelvis
   c. ureter
   d. hilus
   e. pyramid

   Answer: d

7. The renal sinus is
   a. the innermost layer of kidney tissue
   b. a conical-shaped structure that is located in the renal medulla
   c. an internal cavity lined by the fibrous capsule and located in the area of the hilus
   d. a large branch of the renal pelvis
   e. a knot of capillaries that lies within the renal corpuscle

   Answer: c

8. The outermost layer of kidney tissue is the
   a. renal cortex
   b. renal medulla
   c. major calyx
   d. minor calyx
   e. renal pelvis

   Answer: a

9. The innermost layer of kidney tissue is the
   a. renal cortex
   b. renal medulla
   c. major calyx
   d. minor calyx
   e. renal pelvis

   Answer: b

10. Conical-shaped structures that are located in the renal medulla are called
    a. pyramids
    b. renal columns
    c. renal pelvises
    d. nephrons
    e. calyces

    Answer: a

11. Renal columns are
    a. internal cavities of the fibrous capsule located in the area of the hilus
    b. the expanded ends of the ureters
    c. the basic functional units of the kidney
    d. bundles of tissue that lie between pyramids and extend from the renal cortex toward the renal sinus
    e. conical-shaped structures that are located in the renal medulla

    Answer: d

12. The expanded end of the ureter forms the
    a. renal sinus
    b. renal pelvis
    c. renal calyx
    d. renal hilus
    e. renal corpuscle

    Answer: b

13. Major calyces are
    a. large branches of the renal pelvis
    b. expanded ends of nephrons
    c. basic functional layers of the kidney
    d. conical-shaped structures that are located in the renal medulla
    e. the expanded ends of renal pyramids

    Answer: a

14. The Bowman's capsule and glomerulus make up the
    a. renal pyramid
    b. loop of Henle
    c. renal corpuscle
    d. renal tubule system
    e. collecting system

    Answer: c

15. The basic functional unit of the kidney is the
    a. nephron
    b. renal corpuscle
    c. glomerulus
    d. loop of Henle
    e. filtration unit

    Answer: a

16. The expanded end of a nephron is the
    a. glomerulus
    b. Bowman's capsule
    c. proximal convoluted tubule
    d. distal convoluted tubule
    e. loop of Henle

Answer: b

17. A glomerulus is
    a. the expanded end of a nephron
    b. a knot of capillaries that lies within the renal corpuscle
    c. the portion of the nephron closest to the renal corpuscle
    d. the portion of the nephron that attaches to the collecting duct
    e. the horseshoe-shaped segment of the nephron

Answer: b

18. The portion of the tubule system of the nephron closest to the renal corpuscle is the
    a. loop of Henle
    b. proximal convoluted tubule
    c. distal convoluted tubule
    d. collecting duct
    e. minor calyx

Answer: b

19. The portion of the nephron that attaches to the collecting duct is the
    a. proximal convoluted tubule
    b. loop of Henle
    c. distal convoluted tubule
    d. collecting duct
    e. minor calyx

Answer: c

20. The portion of the nephron between Bowman's capsule and the loop of Henle is the
    a. proximal convoluted tubule
    b. renal corpuscle
    c. distal convoluted tubule
    d. collecting duct
    e. minor calyx

Answer: a

21. The process of urine formation involves
    a. filtration of plasma
    b. reabsorption of water
    c. secretion of additional wastes
    d. a and b only
    e. all of the above

Answer: e

22. The primary function of the proximal convoluted tubule
    a. filtration
    b. absorption of ions, organic molecules, vitamins, and water
    c. secretion of acids and ammonia
    d. secretion of drugs
    e. adjusting the urine volume

Answer: b

23. The following is a list of the blood vessels that carry blood to the kidney.
    1. afferent arteriole
    2. arcuate artery
    3. interlobar artery
    4. renal artery
    5. glomerulus
    6. interlobular artery
    7. efferent arteriole
    8. peritubular capillary

    The proper order in which blood passes through these vessels is
    a. 4,6,2,3,1,5,7,8
    b. 4,3,2,6,1,5,7,8
    c. 4,3,2,6,7,5,1,8
    d. 4,6,2,3,7,5,1,8
    e. 4,3,6,2,1,5,7,8

Answer: b

24. The process of filtration occurs at the
    a. proximal convoluted tubule
    b. distal convoluted tubule
    c. collecting duct
    d. loop of Henle
    e. Bowman's capsule

Answer: e

25. The most selective pores in the filtration membrane are located in the
    a. capillary endothelium
    b. lamina densa
    c. podocytes
    d. basement membrane of the capillaries
    e. capsular space

Answer: c

26. Substances larger than _____ are normally not allowed to pass through the filtration membrane.
    a. sodium ions
    b. glucose
    c. albumin
    d. amino acids
    e. urea

Answer: c

27. The process of filtration is driven by
    a. active transport
    b. blood osmotic pressure
    c. renal pumping
    d. blood hydrostatic pressure
    e. solvent drag

Answer: d

28. The ability to form a concentrated urine depends on the functions of the
    a. proximal convoluted tubule
    b. collecting duct
    c. distal convoluted tubule
    d. loop of Henle
    e. Bowman's capsule

Answer: d

29. The cells of the proximal convoluted tubule normally reabsorb
    a. approximately 60% of the volume of the filtrate produced in the renal corpuscle
    b. virtually all of the glucose and other nutrients under normal conditions
    c. cations such as sodium, calcium, and magnesium
    d. anions such as bicarbonate, chloride, sulfate, and phosphate
    e. all of the above

Answer: e

30. Substances secreted by the distal convoluted tubule include
    a. hydrogen ions
    b. potassium ions
    c. creatinine
    d. penicillin
    e. all of the above

    Answer: e

31. When the level of ADH (antidiuretic hormone) increases
    a. more urine is produced
    b. less urine is produced
    c. less water is reabsorbed by the nephron and collecting duct
    d. the specific gravity of the urine decreases
    e. more salt is secreted by the nephron

    Answer: b

32. In response to increased levels of aldosterone, the kidneys produce
    a. a larger volume of urine
    b. urine with a higher concentration of sodium ions
    c. urine with a lower concentration of potassium ions
    d. urine with a lower specific gravity
    e. urine with less urea

    Answer: d

33. Each of the following is a characteristic of a normal urine sample
    except one. Identify the exception.
    a. amber color
    b. cloudy appearance
    c. acidic pH
    d. specific gravity greater than 1.0
    e. odor of ammonia

    Answer: b

34. Each of the following is a normal constituent of urine **except** one.
    Identify the exception.
    a. hydrogen ions
    b. urea
    c. large proteins
    d. salts
    e. creatinine

    Answer: c

35. The ureters and urinary bladder are lined by
    a. stratified squamous epithelium
    b. pseudostratified columnar epithelium
    c. simple cuboidal epithelium
    d. transitional epithelium
    e. simple columnar epithelium

Answer: d

36. The region of the urinary bladder bounded by the exits of the ureters
    and the entrance to the urethra is the
    a. ureter muscle
    b. trigone
    c. bladder flaps
    d. ureteric flap
    e. internal sphincter

Answer: b

37. Which of the following is greater?
    a. the length of the urethra in males
    b. the length of the urethra in females

Answer: a

38. The detrusor muscle
    a. moves urine through the ureters
    b. compresses the urinary bladder and expels urine through the urethra
    c. functions as the internal urinary sphincter
    d. functions as the external urinary sphincter
    e. is located in the renal pelvis

Answer: b

39. During the micturition reflex,
    a. stimulation of stretch receptors in the bladder wall result in
       afferent impulses arriving in the lumbar region of the spinal cord
    b. there is increased activity of the parasympathetic motor neurons that
       control the smooth muscle of the bladder
    c. the internal sphincter must be consciously relaxed
    d. the external sphincter relaxes as the result of a parasympathetic
       reflex
    e. all of the above

Answer: b

40. Each of the following systems of the body is involved in the process of excretion to some degree **except** one. Identify the exception.
    a. urinary system
    b. integumentary system
    c. digestive system
    d. endocrine system
    e. respiratory system

    Answer: d

41. The intracellular fluid (ICF) is found
    a. in blood vessels
    b. in lymph
    c. in the cells of the body
    d. in the interstitial spaces
    e. in the cerebrospinal fluid

    Answer: c

42. The components of extracellular fluid (ECF) include
    a. blood plasma
    b. interstitial fluid
    c. cerebrospinal fluid
    d. a and b only
    e. all of the above

    Answer: e

43. The principal cation in the ICF is
    a. sodium
    b. potassium
    c. calcium
    d. magnesium
    e. chloride

    Answer: b

44. When water is lost but electrolytes are retained
    a. the osmolarity of the ECF falls
    b. osmosis moves water from the ICF to the ECF
    c. both the ECF and the ICF become more dilute
    d. there is an increase in the volume of the ICF
    e. all of the above

    Answer: b

45. When large amounts of pure water are consumed
    a. the ECF becomes hypertonic to the ICF
    b. a fluid shift occurs and the volume of the ICF decreases
    c. osmolarities of the two compartments will be slightly lower
    d. the volume of the ECF will decrease
    e. the volume of the ICF will decrease

    Answer: c

46. Consuming a meal high in salt will
    a. drastically increase the osmolarity of the blood
    b. result in a temporary increase in blood volume
    c. decrease thirst
    d. cause hypotension
    e. activate the renin-angiotensin mechanism

    Answer: b

47. The hormone ADH
    a. is secreted by the anterior pituitary gland in response to changes in blood osmolarity
    b. stimulates the kidneys to retain sodium ion
    c. stimulates water conservation at the kidneys
    d. causes the kidneys to produce a large volume of urine
    e. all of the above

    Answer: c

48. Aldosterone
    a. is secreted in response to elevated levels of sodium in the blood
    b. promotes sodium retention in the kidneys
    c. helps decrease blood volume
    d. increases the concentration of sodium in urine
    e. functions in pH regulation

    Answer: b

49. When the level of sodium ion in the ECF decreases
    a. osmoreceptors are stimulated
    b. a person experiences an increased thirst
    c. more ADH is released
    d. there is an increase in the level of aldosterone
    e. there is an increase in the level of atrial natriuretic peptide

    Answer: d

50. When the amount of sodium ion in the ECF increases
    a. osmoreceptors are stimulated
    b. there is a decreased thirst
    c. ADH secretion decreases
    d. aldosterone secretion increases
    e. there is an increase in the volume of urine produced

    Answer: a

51. Excess potassium ion is eliminated from the body by
    a. sweating
    b. the kidneys
    c. the liver
    d. the digestive system
    e. the spleen

    Answer: b

52. The amount of potassium secreted by the kidneys is regulated by
    a. ADH
    b. aldosterone
    c. parathormone
    d. atrial natriuretic peptide
    e. cortisol

    Answer: b

53. Calcium homeostasis primarily reflects
    a. a balance between absorption in the gut and excretion at the kidneys
    b. careful regulation of blood calcium levels by the kidneys
    c. an interplay between parathormone and aldosterone
    d. an interplay between reserves in the bone, the rate of absorption,
       and the rate of excretion
    e. hormonal control of calcium reserves in the bones

    Answer: d

54. Calcium reabsorption at the kidneys is promoted by the hormone
    a. calcitonin
    b. calcitriol
    c. aldosterone
    d. cortisol
    e. ADH

    Answer: b

55. Each of the following statements concerning chloride ions is true
    except one. Identify the exception.
    a. Chloride ions are the most abundant anions in the ECF.
    b. Chloride ion concentrations in the ICF are usually low.
    c. Chloride ions are absorbed along the digestive tract in the company
       of sodium ions.
    d. Large amounts of chloride ion are lost each day in the urine.
    e. Chloride ions are lost in perspiration.

    Answer: d

56. The most important factor affecting the pH of body fluids is the
    concentration of
    a. lactic acid
    b. ketone bodies
    c. organic acids
    d. carbon dioxide
    e. hydrochloric acid

    Answer: d

57. Changes in the pH of body fluids are compensated for by
    a. protein buffers
    b. the carbonic acid-bicarbonate buffer system
    c. the phosphate buffer system
    d. changes in the rate and depth of breathing
    e. all of the above

    Answer: e

58. Hypoventilation would cause
    a. respiratory acidosis
    b. respiratory alkalosis
    c. metabolic acidosis
    d. metabolic alkalosis
    e. none of the above

    Answer: a

59. In response to respiratory alkalosis
    a. the respiratory rate increases
    b. the tidal volume increases
    c. the kidneys conserve bicarbonate
    d. the kidneys secrete more hydrogen ions
    e. the body retains more carbon dioxide

    Answer: e

60. Prolonged vomiting can result in
    a. respiratory acidosis
    b. respiratory alkalosis
    c. metabolic acidosis
    d. metabolic alkalosis
    e. none of the above

    Answer: d

61. A person who suffers from emphysema can exhibit signs of
    a. respiratory acidosis
    b. respiratory alkalosis
    c. metabolic acidosis
    d. metabolic alkalosis
    e. none of the above

    Answer: a

62. A person who suffers from chronic diabetes can exhibit signs of
    a. respiratory acidosis
    b. respiratory alkalosis
    c. metabolic acidosis
    d. metabolic alkalosis
    e. none of the above

    Answer: c

63. A mountain climber at high altitude may lose consciousness as the result of
    a. respiratory acidosis
    b. respiratory alkalosis
    c. metabolic acidosis
    d. metabolic alkalosis
    e. none of the above

    Answer: b

64. A person who chronically consumes large amounts of antacids to settle an upset stomach may risk
    a. respiratory acidosis
    b. respiratory alkalosis
    c. metabolic acidosis
    d. metabolic alkalosis
    e. none of the above

    Answer: d

65. Changes that occur in the urinary system with aging include all of the
    following **except** one. Identify the exception.
    a. the number of functional nephrons declines
    b. a reduction in the GFR (glomerular filtration rate)
    c. increased sensitivity to ADH
    d. problems with the micturition reflex
    e. loss of sphincter muscle tone

    Answer: c

66. Which of the following is greater?
    a. the amount of ADH released when blood osmolarity is high
    b. the amount of ADH released when blood osmolarity is low

    Answer: a

67. Factors that increase the secretion of ADH include
    a. increased concentration of sodium ions in the ECF
    b. water deprivation
    c. increased osmolarity of the ECF
    d. decreased renal blood flow
    e. all of the above

    Answer: e

68. Dehydration would cause
    a. fluid to shift from the ECF to the ICF
    b. decreased secretion of ADH
    c. increased thirst
    d. decreased levels of aldosterone
    e. all of the above

    Answer: c

69. In which case is the pH lower?
    a. after hyperventilating
    b. after hypoventilating

    Answer: b

70. Which of the following is greater?
    a. the concentration of solute in the filtrate at the beginning of the
       loop of Henle
    b. the concentration of solute in the filtrate at the bottom of the
       descending limb of the loop of Henle

    Answer: a

71. A pyelogram, an X-ray of the urinary system in which radio-opaque dye is injected into the urinary pathways, can be used to detect
    a. kidney stones
    b. structural abnormalities of the kidney
    c. obstruction of the ureters
    d. tumors or growths in the urinary bladder
    e. all of the above

    Answer: e

72. In a normal kidney, which of the following conditions would cause an increase in the glomerular filtration rate (GFR)?
    a. constriction of the afferent arteriole
    b. a decrease in the pressure of the glomerulus
    c. an increase in the capsular hydrostatic pressure
    d. a decrease in the concentration of plasma proteins in the blood
    e. a decrease in the net glomerular filtration pressure

    Answer: d

73. Desert Dan has been lost in the desert for 2 days with very little water. As a result of this exposure, one would expect to observe
    a. elevated ADH levels
    b. decreased blood concentration
    c. normal urine production
    d. increased blood volume
    e. cells enlarged with fluid

    Answer: a

74. If, through injury, the blood flow to the kidneys decreases, which of the following will occur?
    a. aldosterone secretion will increase
    b. sodium reabsorption will be inhibited
    c. there will be systemic vasodilation
    d. obligatory water reabsorption will decrease
    e. the amount of ADH in the blood will decrease

    Answer: a

75. In response to excess water in the body
    a. antidiuretic hormone is secreted by the anterior pituitary gland
    b. the active transport mechanisms in the ascending limb of the loop of Henle cease functioning
    c. the permeability of the distal convoluted tubules and collecting ducts to water is decreased
    d. the permeability of the ascending limb of the loop of Henle is increased
    e. the glomerular filtration rate is reduced

    Answer: c

76. Ions normally found in urine and plasma include which of the following?
    a. chloride
    b. bicarbonate
    c. potassium
    d. sodium
    e. all of the above

    Answer: e

77. Normal constituents of <u>both</u> urine and plasma include all of the following **except**:
    a. amino acids
    b. glucose
    c. lipids
    d. proteins
    e. none of the above

    Answer: d

78. General characteristics of <u>normal</u> urine include:
    a. specific gravity
    b. bacteria
    c. pH
    d. A and B
    e. A and C

    Answer: e

79. Management of renal failure involves restriction of water and salt intake and reducing caloric intake to a minimum; dietary proteins are also limited. This combination lessens the strain on the urinary system by:
    a. minimizing volume of urine produced
    b. altering the pigments produced
    c. preventing the generation of large quantities of nitrogenous waste products
    d. A and C
    e. all of the above

    Answer: d

80. The term incontinence refers to
    a. the inability to void (expel) urine
    b. the inability to control urination
    c. the inability to control kidney function
    d. the process of urinating
    e. the process of urine production

    Answer: b

81. In individuals with an automatic bladder,
    a. the micturition reflex does not remain intact and voluntary control of the external sphincter is not lost.
    b. the micturition reflex remains intact and voluntary control of the external sphincter is not lost.
    c. the micturition reflex remains intact, but voluntary control of the external sphincter is lost.
    d. the micturition reflex does not remain intact, but voluntary control of the external sphincter is lost.
    e. the micturition reflex remains intact and the individual can prevent reflexive emptying of the bladder.

    Answer: c

82. Organs of the urinary system that are involved with urine transport are the
    a. urethra and ureters
    b. kidneys and bladder
    c. ureters and kidneys
    d. urethra and bladder
    e. kidneys and urethra

    Answer: a

83. Using anatomical terminology, identify the correct order of words that make this a true statement. The _____ kidney extends _____ slightly more than the _____ kidney.
    a. right; superiorly; left
    b. right; inferiorly; left
    c. left; superiorly; right
    d. left; inferiorly; right
    e. right; anteriorly; left

    Answer: c

Matching

84. Match the region of the nephron in the first column with its primary function in the second column.

    _____1. renal corpuscle
    _____2. distal convoluted tubule
    _____3. papillary duct
    _____4. collecting duct
    _____5. proximal convoluted tubule

    A. conduction of urine to minor calyx
    B. reabsorption of ions, vitamins, water, and organics
    C. reabsorption of sodium ions and secretion of acids
    D. reabsorption of water and sodium ions
    E. filtration of plasma to initiate urine formation

    Answer: 1-e, 2-c, 3-a, 4-d, 5-b

85. Match the acid-base disorder in the first column with its characteristic treatment in the second column

     _____1. metabolic acidosis   A. improve ventilation
     _____2. metabolic alkalosis   B. administer bicarbonate
     _____3. respiratory acidosis   C. reduce respiratory rate, allow
                                               rise in P_{CO2}
     _____4. respiratory alkalosis   D. no treatment below 7.55 pH;
                                               above 7.55 administer ammonium
                                             chloride

Answer: 1-b, 2-d, 3-a, 4-c

Fill-In-The-Blank

86. The principal ions in the ECF are _____, _____ and _____.

Answer: sodium, chloride and bicarbonate

87. All of the homeostatic mechanisms that monitor and adjust the composition of body fluids respond to changes in the _____ cellular fluid compartment.

Answer: extra

88. Interacting compounds that prevent alterations in the pH of body fluids is termed a(n) _____ _____.

Answer: buffer system

89. The normal pH range for blood is _____.

Answer: 7.35 to 7.45

90. When the pH falls below 7.35, a state of _____ exists.

Answer: acidosis

91. When the pH rises above 7.45, a state of _____ exists.

Answer: alkalosis

Essay

92. Fred suffers from chronic emphysema. Blood tests show that his blood pH is normal but his bicarbonate levels are elevated significantly. How can this be?

Answer:
As long as the ratio of bicarbonate ion to carbonic acid is 20:1, the pH of body fluids will remain normal. Since Fred's condition is chronic (long term) his body has compensated for the excess carbonic acid (the result of hypercapnia due to poor ventilation) by increasing the amount of bicarbonate to match the elevated level of acid. This process involves the kidneys where some of the excess carbon dioxide is converted into carbonic acid and the carbonic acid is allowed to dissociate. The hydrogen ions are secreted and the newly formed bicarbonate is conserved to maintain a proper buffering capacity.

93. Sylvia is suffering from severe edema in her arms and legs. Her physician prescribes a diuretic (a substance that will increase the volume of urine produced). Why might this help to alleviate Sylvia's problem?

Answer:
Increasing the volume of urine produced would decrease the total blood volume of the body. This in turn would lead to a decreased blood hydrostatic pressure. Edema is frequently the result of hydrostatic pressure of the blood exceeding the opposing forces at the capillaries in the affected area. Depending on the actual cause of the edema, decreasing the blood hydrostatic pressure would decrease edema formation and possibly cause some of the fluid to move from the interstitial space back to the blood.

94. David's grandfather suffers from hypertension. His doctor tells him that part of his problem stems from renal arteriosclerosis. Why would this cause hypertension?

Answer:
Renal hypertension would restrict blood flow to the kidneys and produce renal ischemia. Decreased blood flow and ischemia would trigger the juxtaglomerular apparatus to produce more renin which would lead to elevated levels of angiotensin II and aldosterone. Angiotensin II causes vasoconstriction, increased peripheral resistance and thus increased blood pressure. Aldosterone will promote sodium retention. This would lead to more water retained by the body and an increase in blood volume. This too would contribute to a higher blood pressure. Another factor to consider would be the release of more erythropoietin in response to tissue hypoxia. The erythropoietin would stimulate the formation of red blood cells which would lead to increased blood viscosity and again contribute to the hypertension.

Chapter 20:   The Reproductive System

Multiple Choice

1. The reproductive system
   a. produces and transports gametes
   b. stores and nourishes gametes
   c. produces FSH and LH
   d. a and b only
   e. all of the above

   Answer: d

2. The reproductive system includes all of the following **except**
   a. gonads
   b. ducts that receive and transport the gametes
   c. accessory glands and organs that secrete fluids
   d. external genitalia
   e. all of the above are included in the reproductive system

   Answer: e

3. Projections of the tunica albuginea, known as septa, divide the testis into
   a. seminiferous tubules
   b. straight tubules
   c. lobules
   d. interstitial areas
   e. none of the above

   Answer: c

4. Straight tubules originate at the seminiferous tubules and form a maze of passageways called the
   a. epididymis
   b. ductus deferens
   c. rete testis
   d. efferent ducts
   e. ejaculatory ducts

   Answer: c

5. The spermatic cord is
   a. a bundle of tissue that contains the ductus deferens and the blood vessels, nerves, and lymphatics that serve the testis
   b. a narrow opening that links the scrotal chamber with the peritoneal cavity
   c. the external marking of the boundary between the two chambers of the scrotum
   d. a layer of smooth muscle in the skin of the scrotal sac
   e. a dense layer of connective tissue that surrounds the testis

   Answer: a

6. The dense layer of connective tissue that surrounds the testis is called the
   a. median line
   b. spermatic cord
   c. tunica albuginea
   d. dartos muscle
   e. epididymis

   Answer: c

7. Interstitial cells produce
   a. sperm
   b. FSH
   c. nutrients
   d. androgens
   e. androgen-inhibiting protein

   Answer: d

8. Sperm production occurs in the
   a. ductus deferens
   b. seminiferous tubules
   c. the epididymis
   d. seminal vesicles
   e. the rete testis

   Answer: b

9. Sperm develop from "stem cells" called
   a. spermatogonia
   b. primary spermatocytes
   c. spermatids
   d. secondary spermatocytes
   e. spermatozoa

   Answer: a

10. As developing sperm cells begin the process of meiosis they become
    a. spermatogonia
    b. secondary spermatocytes
    c. spermatids
    d. spermatozoans
    e. Sertoli cells

    Answer: b

11. _____ are formed at the end of meiosis.
    a. Spermatogonia
    b. Primary spermatocytes
    c. Spermatids
    d. Secondary spermatocytes
    e. Spermatozoa

    Answer: c

12. The process of spermiogenesis produces
    a. spermatogonia
    b. primary spermatocytes
    c. spermatids
    d. secondary spermatocytes
    e. spermatozoa

    Answer: e

13. Sperm are moved along the ductus deferens by
    a. hydrostatic force
    b. ciliary action
    c. peristaltic contractions
    d. suction
    e. guide cells

    Answer: c

14. The following is a list of structures of the male reproductive tract.
    1. ductus deferens
    2. urethra
    3. ejaculatory duct
    4. epididymis

    The order in which sperm pass through these structures from the testes to the penis is
    a. 1,3,4,2
    b. 4,3,1,2
    c. 4,1,2,3
    d. 4,1,3,2
    e. 1,4,3,2

    Answer: d

15. The structure that is the site of sperm maturation is
    a. ductus deferens
    b. rete testis
    c. seminal vesicle
    d. epididymis
    e. prostate gland

    Answer: d

16. The structure that carries sperm from the epididymis to the urethra is
the
a. ductus deferens
b. epididymis
c. seminal vesicle
d. ejaculatory duct
e. corpus spongiosum

Answer: a

17. The tubular gland that produces a secretion that contains fructose, is
slightly alkaline and contributes about 60% to the volume of the semen
is the
a. prostate gland
b. bulbourethral gland
c. seminal vesicle
d. corpus cavernosum
e. prenuptial gland

Answer: c

18. The gland that surrounds the urethra at the base of the urinary bladder
and produces an alkaline secretion is the
a. seminal vesicle
b. bulbourethral gland
c. prostate gland
d. prenuptial gland
e. Bartholin's gland

Answer: c

19. The small paired glands at the base of the penis that produce a
lubricating secretion are the
a. seminal vesicles
b. prostate glands
c. prenuptial glands
d. Bartholin's glands
e. bulbourethral glands

Answer: e

20. Semen contains
a. spermatozoans
b. seminal fluid
c. nutrients
d. enzymes
e. all of the above

Answer: e

21. The male organ of copulation is the
    a. urethra
    b. ejaculatory duct
    c. penis
    d. corpora cavernosa
    e. corpus spongiosum

    Answer: c

22. The fold of skin that covers the tip of the penis is the
    a. glans penis
    b. prepuce
    c. corpus spongiosum
    d. corpora cavernosa
    e. penile urethra

    Answer: b

23. The portion of the penis that surrounds the external urethral meatus is
    the
    a. prepuce
    b. glans
    c. corpus spongiosum
    d. corpora cavernosa
    e. corona glandis

    Answer: b

24. The erectile tissue that surrounds the urethra is the
    a. membranous urethra
    b. penile urethra
    c. glans penis
    d. corpus spongiosum
    e. corpora cavernosa

    Answer: d

25. The erectile tissue that is located on the ventral surface of the penis
    is the
    a. membranous urethra
    b. penile urethra
    c. corpus spongiosum
    d. corpora cavernosa
    e. prepuce

    Answer: d

26. The scrotum is
    a. the male organ of copulation
    b. the site of sperm production
    c. erectile tissue of the penis
    d. a fleshy pouch suspended below the base of the penis and anterior to the anus
    e. superior to the glans penis

    Answer: d

27. Functions of testosterone include
    a. promoting the functional maturation of sperm
    b. determining secondary sex characteristics
    c. stimulating overall metabolism and sexual behavior
    d. a and b only
    e. all of the above

    Answer: e

28. The role of the pituitary hormone FSH in males is to
    a. stimulate the interstitial cells to produce testosterone
    b. stimulate the sustentacular cells to produce inhibin
    c. initiate sperm production in the testes
    d. develop and maintain secondary sex characteristics
    e. influence sexual behaviors and sex drive

    Answer: c

29. The pituitary hormone that stimulates the interstitial cells to secrete testosterone is
    a. FSH
    b. LH
    c. ACTH
    d. ADH
    e. GH

    Answer: b

30. The structure that transports the ovum to the uterus is the
    a. uterosacral ligament
    b. vagina
    c. uterine tube
    d. infundibulum
    e. myometrium

    Answer: c

31. The organ that provides mechanical protection and nutritional support
    for the developing embryo is the
    a. vagina
    b. uterine tube
    c. ovary
    d. uterus
    e. cervix

    Answer: d

32. The inferior portion of the uterus that projects into the vagina is the
    a. isthmus
    b. fornix
    c. fundus
    d. body
    e. cervix

    Answer: e

33. The muscular layer of the uterus is the
    a. endometrium
    b. perimetrium
    c. myometrium
    d. uterometrium
    e. sarcometrium

    Answer: c

34. The vagina
    a. serves as a passageway for the elimination of menstrual fluids
    b. receives the penis during coitus
    c. holds spermatozoa prior to their passage to the uterus
    d. forms the lower portion of the birth canal
    e. all of the above

    Answer: e

35. The vagina is
    a. a central space surrounded by the labia minora
    b. the inner lining of the uterus
    c. the inferior portion of the uterus
    d. a muscular tube extending between the uterus and the external
       genitalia
    e. a tube that carries ova from the ovary to the uterus

    Answer: d

36. The vulva includes the
    a. mons pubis
    b. labia majora
    c. labia minora
    d. clitoris
    e. all of the above

    Answer: e

37. In the mammary glands, milk production occurs in the
    a. lobes
    b. lobules
    c. lactiferous ducts
    d. lactiferous sinus
    e. all of the above

    Answer: b

38. The central space bounded by the labia minora is the
    a. fornix
    b. vestibule
    c. hymen
    d. clitoris
    e. isthmus

    Answer: b

39. Fleshy folds that encircle and partially conceal the labia minora and
    vestibular structures are the
    a. fornices
    b. ampullae
    c. labia majora
    d. mons pubises
    e. hymens

    Answer: c

40. The clitoris is
    a. a thin epithelial fold that partially or completely blocks the
       entrance to the vagina
    b. a fleshy fold that encircles the vestibule
    c. a mound of fat that is superior to the pubis
    d. a mass of erectile tissue located at the anterior margin of the labia
       minora
    e. a shallow recess that surrounds the cervical portion of the vagina

    Answer: d

41. The generally dark, pigmented skin that surrounds the nipple is called the
    a. clitoris
    b. fornix
    c. zona pellucida
    d. hymen
    e. areola

    Answer: e

42. Each of the following statements concerning oogenesis is true **except** one. Identify the exception.
    a. At the time of birth, the ovaries contain only primary oocytes.
    b. Ova develop from stem cells called oogonia.
    c. An ovum will only complete meiosis if it is fertilized.
    d. Oogenesis occurs continuously from puberty until menopause.
    e. The first meiotic division is completed just prior to ovulation.

    Answer: d

43. The process of oogenesis produces _____ viable ovum/ova.
    a. 1
    b. 2
    c. 3
    d. 4
    e. 8

    Answer: a

44. The surge in LH that occurs during the middle of the ovarian cycle triggers
    a. follicle maturation
    b. menstruation
    c. ovulation
    d. menopause
    e. pregnancy

    Answer: c

45. A rise in the blood levels of FSH at the beginning of the ovarian cycle is responsible for
    a. follicle maturation
    b. menstruation
    c. ovulation
    d. menopause
    e. pregnancy

    Answer: a

46. The average length of the menstrual cycle is ___ days.
    a. 10
    b. 14
    c. 21
    d. 28
    e. 35

    Answer: d

47. During the proliferative phase of the menstrual cycle
    a. ovulation occurs
    b. a new functional layer is formed in the uterus
    c. secretory glands and blood vessels develop in the endometrium
    d. the old functional layer is sloughed off
    e. the corpus luteum is formed

    Answer: b

48. During the secretory phase of the menstrual cycle
    a. ovulation occurs
    b. a new uterine lining is formed
    c. glands enlarge and accelerate their rates of secretion
    d. the old functional layer is sloughed off
    e. the corpus luteum is formed

    Answer: c

49. During the menses
    a. ovulation occurs
    b. a new uterine lining is formed
    c. secretory glands and blood vessels develop in the endometrium
    d. the old functional layer is sloughed off
    e. the corpus luteum is formed

    Answer: d

50. The principal hormone secreted by the corpus luteum is
    a. LH
    b. FSH
    c. progesterone
    d. estradiol
    e. estrogen

    Answer: c

51. Menstruation is triggered by a drop in the level(s) of
    a. human chorionic gonadotropin
    b. FSH
    c. estrogen and progesterone
    d. LH
    e. relaxin

    Answer: c

52. At puberty in both sexes
    a. levels of FSH and LH increase
    b. gametogenesis begins
    c. secondary sex characteristics begin to appear and a sex drive
       develops
    d. a and c only
    e. all of the above

    Answer: e

53. Emission
    a. occurs under parasympathetic stimulation
    b. begins with peristaltic contractions of the vas deferens
    c. is responsible for propelling spermatozoa into the female
       reproductive tract
    d. involves contractions of the cremaster muscle
    e. all of the above

    Answer: b

54. The process of detumescence is under the control of the
    a. parasympathetic nervous system
    b. sympathetic nervous system
    c. both parasympathetic and sympathetic nervous systems

    Answer: b

55. The process of emission is under the control of the
    a. parasympathetic nervous system
    b. sympathetic nervous system
    c. both parasympathetic and sympathetic nervous systems

    Answer: b

56. The process of arousal is under the control of the
    a. parasympathetic nervous system
    b. sympathetic nervous system
    c. both parasympathetic and sympathetic nervous systems

    Answer: a

57. At menopause
    a. menstrual cycles cease
    b. ovarian cycles cease
    c. "hot flashes" may occur
    d. depression may occur
    e. all of the above

    Answer: e

58. During the male climacteric
    a. sperm production ceases
    b. the penis shrinks
    c. FSH and LH levels rise
    d. sex drive increases
    e. all of the above

    Answer: c

59. For erection and ejaculation to occur
    a. there must be sufficient blood hydrostatic pressure leading to
       erectile tissue
    b. the parasympathetic and sympathetic branches of the nervous system
       must be properly functioning
    c. the urinary sphincters must be closed
    d. a and b only
    e. all of the above

    Answer: e

60. Contraction of the cremaster muscle
    a. causes wrinkling of the scrotal sac
    b. produces an erection
    c. propels sperm through the urethra
    d. moves sperm through the ductus deferens
    e. moves the testes closer to the body cavity

    Answer: e

61. Contraction of the dartos muscle
    a. causes wrinkling of the scrotal sac
    b. produces an erection
    c. propels sperm through the urethra
    d. moves sperm through the ductus deferens
    e. moves the testes closer to the body cavity

    Answer: a

62. In response to parasympathetic stimulation
    a. vessels in the penis dilate
    b. blood flow increases to the erectile tissue
    c. vascular channels in the erectile tissue become engorged with blood
    d. erection occurs
    e. all of the above

    Answer: a

63. Major functions of the accessory glands of the male reproductive system include
    a. activating the spermatozoa
    b. providing nutrients spermatozoa need for motility
    c. propelling spermatozoa and fluids along the reproductive tract
    d. producing buffers
    e. all of the above

    Answer: e

64. Removal of the prostate gland would result in semen
    a. that lacked sperm
    b. with a lower than normal pH
    c. with less fructose
    d. with no lubricating fluids
    e. that lacked androgens

    Answer: b

65. Pelvic inflammatory disease
    a. is frequently caused by sexually transmitted pathogens
    b. causes fever and abdominal pain
    c. can cause sterility
    d. can possibly lead to peritonitis
    e. all of the above

    Answer: e

66. In the follicular phase of the ovarian cycle, the ovary is
    a. undergoing a loss of size
    b. forming the corpus luteum
    c. releasing a mature ovum
    d. secreting progesterone
    e. maturing a follicle

    Answer: e

67. Which of the following is greater?
    a. the number of primordial follicles in the female ovaries at birth
    b. the number of primordial follicles in the female ovaries at puberty

    Answer: a

68. Long-term compression of the spermatic artery and vein could result in
    a. decreased blood flow to the testes
    b. decreased blood levels of testosterone
    c. sterility
    d. impotence
    e. all of the above

    Answer: e

69. Sperm cannot fertilize an egg unless they have been in the female
    reproductive tract for several hours. This enhanced ability of the sperm
    to fertilize the ovum is called capacitation. In vitro studies indicate
    that the sperm can fertilize the ovum if they are first washed before
    being introduced to the ovum. These observations suggest that
    a. the process of capacitation involves the removal of some inhibiting
       substance or substances from the sperm
    b. the process of capacitation is temperature dependent
    c. in capacitation, secretions of the female reproductive tract are
       taken up by the sperm
    d. pH is an important factor in the process of capacitation
    e. only sperm that come into contact with vaginal secretions are capable
       of fertilizing an ovum

    Answer: a

70. Marissa is an avid jogger and she trains incessantly. She has slimmed
    down so that she is now underweight for her height and has very little
    fat tissue. You would expect Marissa to
    a. have heavy menstrual flows
    b. double ovulate
    c. be amenorrheic (no monthly menstrual flow)
    d. have painful menstrual cramps
    e. show elevated levels of FSH

    Answer: c

71. This condition is characterized by failure of the testes to descend into
    the scrotum at the time of birth.
    a. impotence
    b. cryptorchidism
    c. sterility
    d. incontinent
    e. erectile dysfunction

    Answer: b

72. The clinical term for inflammation of the prostate is
    a. glomerulonephritis
    b. testicular hypertrophy
    c. prostatitis
    d. nephritis
    e. follicular hypertrophy

Answer: c

73. Currently, this type of cancer is the second most common cancer in males, and it is the second leading cause of cancer deaths in men.
    a. prostate cancer
    b. testicular cancer
    c. lung cancer
    d. penile cancer
    e. bone cancer

Answer: a

74. The organism responsible for 50% to 80% of pelvic inflammatory disease (PID) infections is:
    a. *Chlamydia trachomatis*
    b. *Ureaplasma urealyticum*
    c. *Chlamydia psittaci*
    d. *Neisseria gonorrhoeae*
    e. *Neisseria meningitidis*

Answer: d

75. Currently, the probable cause of up to 50% of all cases of pelvic inflammatory disease (PID) involves this genus of microorganism
    _____.
    a. *Chlamydia*
    b. *Streptococcus*
    c. *Mycobacterium*
    d. *Neisseria*
    e. *Staphylococcus*

Answer: a

76. Cessation of the normal adult menstrual cycle for 6 months or more is termed
    a. dysfunction
    b. amenorrhea
    c. menarche
    d. puberty
    e. dysmenorrhea

Answer: b

77. Identify the notable risk factor(s) associated with breast cancer.
    a. family history
    b. poor diet
    c. pregnancy after age 30
    d. early menarche
    e. A, C, and D

    Answer: e

78. The most common forms of sexually transmitted diseases include:
    a. syphilis, AIDS, Bordetella, herpes
    b. hepatitis, herpes, pneumonia, and warts
    c. gonorrhea, syphilis, herpes, and chancroid
    d. warts, HIV, herpes, and vibriosis
    e. syphilis, anthrax, gonorrhea, tularemia

    Answer: c

79. The surgical technique used to sterilize a male is termed
    a. tubal ligation
    b. spermatoectomy
    c. penile barrier
    d. vasectomy
    e. none of the above

    Answer: d

80. This birth control strategy interferes with the female hormonal cycle so that ovulation does not occur.
    a. vaginal barrier
    b. intrauterine device (IUD)
    c. rhythm method
    d. diaphragm
    e. oral contraceptives

    Answer: e

Matching

81. Match the hormone in the first column with its primary effect in the second column

    _____1. estrogen
    _____2. inhibin
    _____3. androgen
    _____4. luteinizing hormone
    _____5. gonadotropin-releasing hormone

    A. maintains secondary sex characteristics
    B. stimulates interstitial cells
    C. inhibits secretion of FSH
    D. stimulates LH secretion
    E. stimulates FSH secretion

    Answer: 1-d, 2-c, 3-a, 4-b, 5-e

Fill-In-The-Blank

82. The male gonad is called a _____.

    Answer: testis

83. The _____ muscle is a layer of smooth muscle in the skin of the scrotal sac.

    Answer: dartos

84. Sperm cells are produced by the process of _____.

    Answer: spermatogenesis

85. The _____ is the part of the sperm that contains the chromosomes.

    Answer: head

86. The _____ _____ of the sperm contains microtubules and mitochondria.

    Answer: middle piece

87. The tail of the sperm is actually a(n) _____.

    Answer: flagellum

88. To become active, motile and fully functional, sperm cells must undergo the process of _____.

    Answer: capacitation

89. The junction of the ductus deferens and the base of the seminal vesicle is called the _____ _____.

    Answer: ejaculatory duct

90. The procedure in which the prepuce is removed from the penis is called a(n) _____.

    Answer: circumcision

91. Most of the body of the penis consists of three masses of _____ _____ that become engorged with blood during an erection.

    Answer: erectile tissue

92. The _____ are finger-like projections at the end of the uterine tube.

    Answer: fimbriae

93. The funnel-shaped end of the uterine tube is called the _____.

    Answer: infundibulum

94. The internal orifice connects the uterine cavity to the _____ cavity.

    Answer: cervical

95. The expanded, superior portion of the uterus is called the _____.

    Answer: body

96. The space within the uterus is called the _____ _____.

    Answer: uterine cavity

97. The _____ is the inner lining of the uterus.

    Answer: endometrium

98. The shallow recess that surrounds the cervical protrusion into the vagina is called the _____.

    Answer: fornix

99. _____ _____ are specialized structures within the ovary that contain an oocyte.

    Answer: Ovarian follicles

100. The _____ _____ is a layer of follicle cells that surrounds the oocyte after ovulation.

    Answer: corona radiata

101. _____ is the process of sloughing off the old functional layer of the endometrium.

    Answer: Menstruation

102. The _____ is a thin epithelial fold that partially or completely blocks the entrance to the vagina.

    Answer: hymen

103. _____ _____ are mucous glands that resemble the bulbourethral glands of the male.

    Answer: Vestibular glands

104. The _____ is a small, conical projection where ducts of the mammary glands open onto the body surface.

    Answer: nipple

105. The onset of menstruation at puberty is called _____.

    Answer: menarche

106. The cessation of menstruation that occurs during midlife is called _____.

    Answer: menopause

Essay

107. Jerry is in an automobile accident that severs his spinal cord at the L3 level. After his recovery, he wonders if he will still be able to have an erection. What would you tell him?

    Answer:
    Yes, he would still be able to have an erection. Erection is primarily controlled by a parasympathetic reflex that is controlled by the sacral region of the spinal cord (inferior to the injury). Tactile stimulation of the penis would initiate the parasympathetic reflex that controls erection. He would also be able to experience an erection by a sympathetic route, since this would be controlled in the T12 to L2 area of the cord (superior to the injury). Stimulation by higher centers could produce a decreased sympathetic tone in the vessels to the penis resulting in an erection.

Chapter 21: Development and Inheritance

Multiple Choice

1. Fertilization of the ovum usually occurs
   a. within 1 hour of ovulation
   b. as much as three to four days following ovulation
   c. in the ovary
   d. in the upper 1/3 of the Fallopian tube
   e. in the uterus

   Answer: d

2. Sperm cannot fertilize an egg until
   a. they undergo capacitation
   b. they undergo activation
   c. they lose their acrosome
   d. they are in the vagina for 3 days
   e. all of the above

   Answer: a

3. During amphimixis
   a. sperm become capacitated
   b. the ovum finishes meiosis II
   c. the male and female pronuclei fuse
   d. meiosis occurs
   e. gametes are formed

   Answer: c

4. The period of gestation that is characterized by rapid fetal growth is
   the _____ trimester.
   a. first
   b. second
   c. third

   Answer: c

5. The period of gestation when the rudiments of all major organ systems
   appear is the _____ trimester.
   a. first
   b. second
   c. third

   Answer: a

6. The period of gestation when organs and organ systems complete most of their development and the fetus looks distinctly human is the _____ trimester.
   a. first
   b. second
   c. third

Answer: b

7. The process of cell division that occurs after fertilization is called
   a. cleavage
   b. implantation
   c. placentation
   d. embryogenesis
   e. blastulation

Answer: a

8. The penetration of the endometrium by the blastocyst is referred to as
   a. cleavage
   b. implantation
   c. placentation
   d. embryogenesis
   e. fertilization

Answer: b

9. _____ are identical cells that are produced by early cleavage.
   a. Blastomeres
   b. Morulas
   c. Gastrulas
   d. Amnions
   e. Blastocysts

Answer: a

10. The solid ball of cells that is formed after several rounds of cell division following fertilization is called a
    a. chorion
    b. blastula
    c. gastrula
    d. morula
    e. blastocyst

Answer: d

11. A blastocyst is
    a. an extraembryonic membrane that forms blood vessels
    b. a solid ball of cells
    c. a hollow ball of cells
    d. a portion of the placenta
    e. the membrane that forms the urinary bladder

    Answer: c

12. The inner cell mass of the blastocyst
    a. will form the placenta
    b. will form the morula
    c. will form the embryo
    d. will form blood vessels of the placenta
    e. will provide nutrients for early growth

    Answer: c

13. During implantation
    a. the syncytial trophoblast erodes a path through the endometrium
    b. the inner cell mass begins to form the placenta
    c. maternal blood vessels in the endometrium are walled off from the blastocyst
    d. the entire trophoblast becomes syncytial
    e. the inner cell mass is temporarily deprived of nutrients

    Answer: a

14. Separation of the inner cell mass from the trophoblast forms the
    a. blastocoele
    b. lacunae
    c. amniotic cavity
    d. chorion
    e. allantois

    Answer: c

15. During implantation, the inner cell mass organizes into a(n)
    a. trophoblast
    b. morula
    c. placenta
    d. blastodisc
    e. amniotic sac

    Answer: d

16. During gastrulation
    a. the blastodisc is formed
    b. the placenta is formed
    c. germ layers are formed
    d. cells from the ectoderm move to the endoderm
    e. all of the above

    Answer: c

17. The ectoderm forms
    a. muscle
    b. blood
    c. neural tissues
    d. the lining of the digestive tract
    e. the urinary system

    Answer: c

18. The mesoderm forms
    a. muscle
    b. skin
    c. the brain
    d. the lining of the digestive tract
    e. respiratory epithelium

    Answer: a

19. The chorionic villi
    a. form the umbilical cord
    b. form the umbilical vein
    c. form the umbilical arteries
    d. increase the surface area available for exchange between the placenta
       and the maternal blood
    e. form a portion of the placenta

    Answer: d

20. The endoderm forms
    a. muscle
    b. neural tissue
    c. blood
    d. skin
    e. the digestive lining

    Answer: e

21. The extraembryonic membrane that forms blood is the
    a. yolk sac
    b. amnion
    c. allantois
    d. chorion
    e. decidua

    Answer: a

22. The extraembryonic membrane that forms a fluid-filled sac is the
    a. yolk sac
    b. amnion
    c. allantois
    d. chorion
    e. decidua

    Answer: b

23. The extraembryonic membrane that forms the urinary bladder is the
    a. yolk sac
    b. allantois
    c. amnion
    d. chorion
    e. decidua

    Answer: b

24. The extraembryonic membrane that forms the fetal portion of the placenta is the
    a. yolk sac
    b. amnion
    c. allantois
    d. chorion
    e. decidua

    Answer: d

25. The hormone that is the basis for a pregnancy test is
    a. LH
    b. progesterone
    c. human chorionic gonadotropin (hCG)
    d. human placental lactogen (hPL)
    e. relaxin

    Answer: c

26. During pregnancy
    a. a woman's respiratory rate and tidal volume increase
    b. maternal blood volume increases
    c. maternal nutrient requirements increase
    d. a woman's glomerular filtration rate increases
    e. all of the above

    Answer: e

27. During gestation, powerful uterine contractions are suppressed by
    a. elevated levels of progesterone
    b. elevated levels of estrogen
    c. elevated levels of oxytocin
    d. elevated levels of prostaglandins
    e. all of the above

    Answer: a

28. The first stage of labor is the
    a. dilation stage
    b. expulsion stage
    c. placental stage
    d. decidual stage
    e. neonate stage

    Answer: a

29. The stage of labor during which the fetus emerges from the vagina is called the
    a. emergence stage
    b. dilation stage
    c. placental stage
    d. expulsion stage
    e. fetal stage

    Answer: d

30. During the neonatal period
    a. the pattern of cardiovascular circulation changes from what it was in utero
    b. the typical heart rate is higher than that of an adult
    c. the typical respiratory rate is higher than that of an adult
    d. a and c only
    e. all of the above

    Answer: e

31. At puberty
    a. FSH levels rise
    b. LH levels rise
    c. levels of sex hormones rise
    d. gametogenesis begins
    e. all of the above

    Answer: e

32. As a person ages
    a. hormone levels decrease
    b. bones become more fragile
    c. peristalsis and muscle tone decrease
    d. b and c only
    e. all of the above

    Answer: d

33. Factors involved in senescence include
    a. decrease in the size of some cell populations
    b. accumulation of mutations
    c. decrease in the number of stem cells
    d. a change in genetic activity
    e. all of the above

    Answer: e

34. Paired chromosomes are called
    a. homologous chromosomes
    b. heterozygous chromosomes
    c. homozygous chromosomes
    d. autosomes
    e. alleles

    Answer: a

35. Chromosomes that are not sex chromosomes are called
    a. homologous chromosomes
    b. homozygous chromosomes
    c. heterozygous chromosomes
    d. autosomes
    e. alleles

    Answer: d

36. The various forms of any one gene are called
    a. homologous chromosomes
    b. homozygous chromosomes
    c. heterozygous chromosomes
    d. autosomes
    e. alleles

    Answer: e

37. If an individual carries a pair of alleles that are the same they are
    _____ for the trait.
    a. homologous
    b. homozygous
    c. heterozygous
    d. autosomal
    e. polygenic

    Answer: b

38. If an individual carries two different alleles for the same trait they
    are
    a. homologous
    b. homozygous
    c. heterozygous
    d. autosomal
    e. polygenic

    Answer: c

39. Recessive x-linked traits
    a. are passed from fathers to their sons
    b. are more likely to be expressed in males
    c. always affect some aspect of the reproductive system
    d. are never expressed in females
    e. cannot be passed from mothers to daughters

    Answer: b

40. In simple inheritance
    a. phenotypic characters are determined by a single pair of alleles
    b. phenotypic characters are determined by multiple alleles
    c. phenotypic characters are determined by the action of a single gene
    d. phenotypic characters are controlled by regulator genes on a
       chromosome other than the one that has the structural genes
    e. phenotypic characters are determined by the genes on the Y chromosome

    Answer: a

41. In polygenic inheritance
    a. phenotypic characters are determined by a single pair of alleles
    b. phenotypic characters are determined by multiple alleles
    c. phenotypic characters are determined by the action of a single gene
    d. phenotypic characters are always controlled by genes on the same chromosome
    e. phenotypic characters are determined by the genes on the Y chromosome

    Answer: b

42. A normally pigmented woman whose father was an albino marries a normally pigmented man whose mother was an albino. What is the probability that they would have an albino child?
    a. 1/2
    b. 1/4
    c. 1/8
    d. 1/16
    e. 100%

    Answer: b

43. A color blind man marries a woman who is heterozygous for the trait. What proportion of their sons, if they have any, can be expected to be color blind?
    a. 1/2
    b. 1/4
    c. 1/8
    d. 100%
    e. 0

    Answer: a

44. If a sperm cell lacked sufficient quantities of hyaluronidase, it would not be able to
    a. move its flagellum
    b. penetrate the corona radiata
    c. become capacitated
    d. survive the environment of the female reproductive tract
    e. metabolize fructose

    Answer: b

45. Problems involving the formation of the chorion would affect
    a. the embryo's ability to produce blood cells
    b. the formation of limbs
    c. the embryo's ability to derive nutrients from the mother
    d. lung formation
    e. the urinary system

    Answer: c

46. Stretching of the cervix would cause an increase in the blood levels of
    a. estrogen
    b. progesterone
    c. oxytocin
    d. relaxin
    e. chorionic gonadotropin

    Answer: c

47. Maternal blood volume increases during pregnancy because
    a. hypoxia resulting from fetal demand for oxygen stimulates release of erythropoietin
    b. decreased peripheral blood volume due to circulation in the placenta leads to the release of renin
    c. increased aldosterone secretion promotes salt and water retention at the kidneys
    d. decreased venous return due to blood volume diverted to the placenta triggers a compensating mechanism
    e. all of the above

    Answer: e

48. Assisted reproductive technologies (ART) are approaches used to solve problems of
    a. sterility
    b. infertility
    c. impotence
    d. adoption
    e. pregnancy

    Answer: b

49. Changes associated with postnatal development include
    a. nail formation, alveolar formation, and myelination
    b. ossification, peripheral receptor formation, and degeneration of embryonic kidneys
    c. myelination, alveoli inflate, and immune system becomes operative
    d. adrenal gland formation, nostrils open, and epiphyseal plate formation
    e. muscle mass increases, epidermal layers appear, and genitalia form

    Answer: c

50. Polygenic traits include
    a. eye color and hair colors other than pure blond or red
    b. albinism and brachydactyly
    c. inability to roll the tongue into a U-shape
    d. curly hair and eye color
    e. blood Rh factor and color blindness

    Answer: a

51. A condition associated with a sex-linked trait is
    a. albinism
    b. red hair
    c. eye color
    d. color blindness
    e. ability to taste phenylthiocarbamate (PTC)

    Answer: d

52. Identify the relatively common <u>autosomal recessive</u> disorder.
    a. Duchenne's muscular dystrophy
    b. cystic fibrosis
    c. Huntington's disease
    d. Myotonic muscular dystrophy
    e. all of the above

    Answer: b

53. The transmission of genetic information from generation to generation is
    termed
    a. inheritance
    b. polygenics
    c. capacitation
    d. development
    e. embryology

    Answer: a

54. The process by which sex cells are formed is called
    a. gastrulation
    b. cleavage
    c. meiosis
    d. mitosis
    e. respiration

    Answer: c

55. The genotype for a <u>male</u> would be:
    a. XX
    b. XO
    c. XXO
    d. XY
    e. XYY

    Answer: d

56. The purpose of the Human Genome Project (HGP) is to:
    a. identify alleles for research
    b. transcribe all the human chromosomes and genes
    c. discover new methods for finger printing
    d. create a "master race"
    e. study human development

    Answer: b

Matching

57. Match the primary germ layer in the first column with its developmental contribution to the body listed in the second column.

    _____1. ectoderm   A. components of nearly all of the muscular system
    _____2. endoderm   B. components of all neural tissue
    _____3. mesoderm   C. components of the urinary bladder and distal portions of the duct system

    Answer: 1-b, 2-c, 3-a

Fill-In-The-Blank

58. _____ is the period of intrauterine development.

    Answer: Gestation

59. The outer layer of blastocyst cells that provide nourishment for the embryo is the _____.

    Answer: trophoblast

60. The hollow cavity within the blastocyst is the _____.

    Answer: blastocoele

61. During the process of _____ the body organs begin to form.

    Answer: organogenesis

62. The process of forming a placenta is called _____.

    Answer: placentation

63. The process by which a viable embryo is formed is called _____.

    Answer: embryogenesis

64. The _____ _____ is formed by the allantois, blood vessels and yolk sac.

    Answer: umbilical cord

65. The blood vessels that carry blood to the placenta are the _____ _____.

    Answer: umbilical arteries

66. The blood vessel that carries blood away from the placenta is the _____ _____.

    Answer: umbilical vein

67. Contractions that are neither regular nor persistent and that occur before the end of gestation are called _____ _____.

    Answer: false labor

68. Parturition is the process of _____.

    Answer: birth or delivery

69. In a(n) _____ _____, an incision large enough to allow for the passage of an infant's head is made through the abdominal wall and uterus.

    Answer: caesarian section

70. The period from birth to the end of the first month is known as the _____ period.

    Answer: neonatal

71. The period from one month to two years is known as _____.

    Answer: infancy

72. The period from two years to puberty is known as _____.

    Answer: childhood

73. Human gametes contain _____ chromosomes.

    Answer: 23

74. Human somatic cells contain _____ chromosomes.

    Answer: 46 or 23 pair of

75. An individual's entire genetic makeup is called his/her _____.

    Answer: genotype

76. The genes that are expressed in an individual produce the _____.

    Answer: phenotype

77. A _____ allele will always be expressed regardless of what the other allele happens to be.

    Answer: dominant

78. A _____ allele is only expressed in the homozygous condition.

    Answer: recessive

79. The _____ _____ is a simple box diagram that allows us to predict the probability of a particular trait occurring in the offspring of a given mating.

    Answer: Punnett square

80. _____ chromosomes are responsible for determining an individual's sex.

    Answer: Sex

81. Genes that appear on the X chromosome are said to be _____.

    Answer: x-linked

82. A person whose genotype is XX would be a _____.

    Answer: female

83. A person whose genotype is XY would be a _____.

    Answer: male

84. _____ is a technique in which a sample of amniotic fluid is analyzed to determine the presence of genetic defects in the fetus.

    Answer: Amniocentesis

85. _____ _____ _____ is a procedure in which cells collected from the villi are analyzed for genetic defects.

    Answer: Chorionic villus sampling

Essay

86. Joe and Jane desperately want to have children, and although they have tried for two years, they have not been successful. Finally, each of them consults a physician, and it turns out that Joe suffers from oligospermia (a low sperm count). He confides to you that he doesn't understand why this would interfere with his ability to have children since he remembers from biology class that it only takes one sperm to fertilize an egg. What would you tell him?

Answer:
Although technically what Joe says is true, it only takes one sperm to fertilize an egg, the probability of this occurring if not enough sperm are deposited is very slim. Of the millions of sperm that enter the female reproductive tract, most are killed or disabled before they reach the uterus. The acid environment, temperature, and presence of immunoglobulins in the vaginal secretions are just a few of the factors responsible for the demise of so many sperm. Once inside of the uterus, there is still a long way to go and many sperm are not capable of making the complete trip to the egg. Once at the egg, the sperm must penetrate the layers of cells that surround it and this requires the combined enzyme contribution of perhaps one hundred sperm or more. If the man begins this process with too few sperm, the chance that enough will reach the egg to penetrate through to the egg membrane is very slim.